BROKEN PROMISES

Why Canadian Medicare Is in Trouble
And What Can Be Done to Save It

BROKEN PROMISES

*Why Canadian Medicare
is in Trouble
and what can be done
to save it*

Les Vertesi M.D.

Belleville, Ontario, Canada

BROKEN PROMISES
Copyright © 2003, Les Vertesi

National Library of Canada Cataloguing in Publication

Vertesi, Les, 1946-
  Broken promises : why Canadian medicare is in trouble and what
can be done to save it / Les Vertesi.

ISBN 1-55306-552-2

  1. Health care reform--Canada. 2. Medical care--Canada. I. Title.

RA395.C3V47 2003   362.1'0971
C2003-900070-2

For more information or
to order additional copies, please contact:

Dr. Les Vertesi
Internet: www.brokenpromises.ca
E-mail: info@brokenpromises.ca

Epic Press is an imprint of *Essence Publishing.*
For more information, contact:
44 Moira Street West, Belleville, Ontario, Canada K8P 1S3
Phone: 1-800-238-6376 • Fax: (613) 962-3055
E-mail: info@essencegroup.com • Internet: www.essencegroup.com

Printed in Canada
by

TABLE OF CONTENTS

THE LETTER

Dear Administrators:

Please accept this letter of concern regarding a patient that I managed yesterday. I was the emergency physician on duty at the Health Care Centre here in Whistler in the evening when Mr. R.C. was brought in by ambulance. He had collapsed in his bathroom after getting out of a hot tub after a day of skiing and presented with severe headache and bleeding from his right ear. He was completely awake when I saw him, but could not remember falling and was disoriented to time and date. He had bright red blood dripping from his right ear without an obvious external laceration or other source. Blood tests and skull X-rays were normal.

Clinically, I felt this man must have a basal skull fracture, but I could not tell whether his head injury was a result of the fall, or whether he had an intra-cranial bleed that had caused the collapse in the first place. Since he was still disoriented, I was concerned that he might have further bleeding in his head as a result of the injury. These questions could only be answered by a CT scan, which was urgently needed. As you know, there is no CT scanner in our community.

I called the neurologist at Vancouver General Hospital who thought it was a neurosurgical problem and suggested that I call the neurosurgeon. I was able to contact the neurosurgeon who agreed it might be neurosurgical, but informed me that he had no beds and that the alternate trauma hospital in the area also had no neurosurgical beds. He tried to reassure me that basal skull fractures rarely result in any problems.

I then called a neurosurgeon at Lions Gate Hospital who told me he also had no beds and could not accept the patient. He suggested my patient would probably be OK at least until the morning and asked if I would consider overnight hospitalization at our local hospital. I explained to him that this hospital has no CT scanner, no in-house physicians, no specialists and limited nursing staff for a potentially critical patient. After stressing that I felt the patient at least deserved a CT scan tonight he suggested I call the neurologist to see if he might have a bed and be able to do a scan. I talked next to the neurologist at this hospital who said that under no circumstances could he accept this patient, because if it turned out to be a surgical problem his neurosurgeon would not be able to cope with it if no beds were available. I then called the neurosurgeon at the alternate trauma hospital, knowing there were no beds, but hoping the surgeon would take my patient anyway. He also denied my request.

My last option was to call Harborview Medical Center in Seattle. My patient was accepted there by the neurosurgeon on call and after talking to the trauma doctor there, the transport was quickly organized and the U.S. Air Ambulance agreed to meet us at Vancouver International Airport. I requested a helicopter from our provincial Air-Evac service, but it was denied due to poor weather. By this time it was almost 11 p.m. so I requested a 'stat' transfer by road ambulance instead. It arrived one hour later and by 0015 we were on the road with the patient.

I decided to accompany him in the ambulance in case his condition worsened and I brought along the medicine and equipment I *might need for a rapid intubation. Even by the time we started the transport, my patient was becoming less conscious and when we entered Vancouver he was no longer responding at all. I did not feel it was safe to continue with the transport to Seattle. It was now two a.m. and I had to call the neurosurgeon again at the General, and was told to proceed to their hospital in spite of the previous refusal. After a brief review there in the ER he went for a CT scan, which showed a large epidermal haematoma pressing on his brain. He was taken from the scanner straight to the operating room and is now in the intensive care unit. Had I carried on to Seattle, he would not have survived.*

My colleagues and I urge each of you in positions of influence to review this case seriously. Please do not let us be placed into a similar position again.

Sincerely.

M.R. (Emergency Physician)

INTRODUCTION

What is it with Canadians and their system of health care? The Romanow report insists it is the best health care system in the world, and needs only a few adjustments and a bit more money. Others, such as the Senate report by Kirby warn that it is unsustainable and needs major structural changes to avoid a complete collapse. As far back as 1995, a federal task force on health care concluded that the system was basically sound and there was enough money, but that some 'efficiencies' could be found. Publications such as "Canadian Health Care—a System in Collapse" from the Fraser Institute claim it has fallen down on virtually all of its promises. The Tommy Douglas Research Institute's report released in early 2001 believed that the system was basically sound but needed to move further in the direction of community clinics and salaried physicians. The Fyke report from Saskatchewan in the spring of 2001 saw tremendous waste in the system, and suggested that further hospital closures were necessary to prevent runaway costs. Headlines in one newspaper in July 2001 read, "Canadians worried about health care"

while another major newspaper claimed "Canadians satisfied with their health care" and both were quoting the same study. There seems to be no end of studies showing one thing or another about our health care system. If so many experts cannot agree on what is going on, what are regular people supposed to believe?

For one thing, they can look at their own experiences. Those unlucky enough to need health care will either have had an excellent experience with no cost or inconvenience, or they may be one of those unfortunate ones caught up in the waiting lists and crowded emergency rooms that increasingly mark our health-care system. It is largely a matter of luck on any given day, although there is no mistaking the trend toward increasing congestion, unconscionable delays and straightforward inability to obtain services. If we were talking about failing to provide the most recent advances in health care or some of the experimental and high-tech services, that would be one thing. Increasingly, the services Canadians are unable to get are the routine, everyday ones, such as an appendectomy or a repair of a simple fracture or a D&C for menstrual bleeding.

They could also ask any health-care provider. Whether they talk to a nurse, a doctor or an X-ray technician, they will find an aging, alienated workforce tired of always compensating for the increasing volumes and inadequacies of the system in which they work. Politicians watch costs escalate and wonder why services seem to deteriorate even as their funding commitment increases. It doesn't matter much where one looks—the indications of trouble are hard to miss.

The fact is, Canadians still rank their health-care system among their top priorities and increasingly they are becoming worried that it will not be there for them when they need it. For most Canadians, reared on the promise of a social safety net, medicare is increasingly looking like nothing more than a series of broken promises. It is right to worry. At the present rate, our costs will soon consume more than half of the typical provincial budget. Our physicians and nurses will soon reach retirement age without ready replacements, our hospitals will be unable to buy or maintain their aging equipment, and the salaries demanded by those workers who are still left will force our hospitals into virtual bankruptcy. All of this will happen just as the boomer generation begins to succumb to age-related illness, technology stretches human life into a prolonged nursing-home experience, and the consumer generation, nourished on the public trough of entitlement, grows into its age of political influence.

Everyone agrees that something must be done, but those who expect that change can occur without some substantial trade-offs should think again. Unfortunately simply agreeing that change is necessary is not good enough. It is important to know where that change is going, because in the end, that will determine whether we will make things better or worse.

Which leads us to why I wrote this book. If we don't know how we got here, how can we know how to get ourselves out? If we don't know how the problems were created, how do we know whether the changes we make will help, or make the problem even worse? The answers to these questions will never be answered by a snapshot at the numbers. They are buried deep within the dynamic of our history.

This book will argue that Canadian medicare, as currently practiced, is built on a set of economic assumptions that are a product of the 1950s, which have remained essentially unchanged since that time. These assumptions form an economic model that does not work and has been discredited in every other country in which it has been tried. It will argue that the Canada Health Act, far from guaranteeing access as it was supposed to do, is actually *impeding* access, cementing existing vested interests and essentially destroying that which it was set up to protect. It will maintain, furthermore, that the paradigm feeds a vicious cycle that resists change because the very people needed to make the change have become part of the problem. And finally, it will offer the suggestion that there are ways to achieve our original objectives of universal access, provided we are prepared to jettison some of the accompanying baggage. Whether we reach this point before sustaining irreparable damage will depend on how quickly we pay attention to the lessons of history, and on how quickly we can bring ourselves to act.

The book is divided into three parts to make easier reading. *The Landscape* begins giving us a little history and a few of the economic fundamentals needed to understand the argument. The second section, entitled *The Players,* traces the recent history of each of the major stakeholder groups that make up our "system," identifies their natural interests, and describes where we can expect them to sit on the issues. And in the last section I will offer a 'diagnosis' and a 'prescription' of ten suggestions that would rescue the central purpose of our system—which is to make sure we all get care when we get sick without turning us all into Americans, and without bankrupting ourselves. Some chapters are of necessity more technical than others, and those readers who find some of the detail tedious or not relevant to them should feel free to jump forward to the parts that offer the most interest.

All of the clinical anecdotes are true, most taken from my own experience as a career emergency physician. While they have been selected for their interest, they are not particularly unusual and any clinician could surely add others almost indefinitely. They serve only to connect my remarks and to underscore what I am talking about.

Since this is a book aimed at ordinary people rather than academics, I promise to use as few formulas and numbers as possible, and to explain my arguments with examples wherever I can. As a physician and a researcher, I am acutely aware that graphs and numbers can be used to bolster almost any argument one chooses. Therefore, instead of showing theories and formulas, I will rely on a historical tracing of how medicare was built, trusting that the overview offered by hindsight will make my points clear. I expect this departure from the convention of graphs and tables may annoy some of my more academic colleagues, but if that is what it costs to meet my objective of reaching ordinary Canadians, then I am prepared to take that criticism.

I do offer one caution. The progression of historical events was not a smooth one and would, of necessity, have varied somewhat, depending on which province and which area of the country one is considering. In that sense, no single historical picture can ever be completely accurate. I know that I open myself to criticism, since one can always find an exception somewhere, or a difference in the actual sequence of events. And yet, all provinces started at more or less the same place before medicare began and ended up with almost identical difficulties. The conclusion that our problems are caused by something in common—either in our assumptions or in the constraints we face—is inescapable. Naturally, since I come from British Columbia, I use more examples from this part of the country. I try, however, when tracing historical events, to use situations common to all the provinces, and will do my best to avoid getting lost in the detail of who-did-what-first and who-did-what-second. I believe it is not the detail that will help us find the difficulties but the common themes, and it is these common points that I try to emphasize.

What most people do not appreciate is that our health-care system is more than just a mechanism to look after sick people. It is also a great battleground for some of the most pervasive ideologies of mankind, which explains why the debate is so heated. For many people, much more is at stake than just health care. While this book may not convince everyone of the final answer, I hope it will at least establish the context, and explain the predicament and why we are faced with such a differing array of expert advice.

The rest will be up to us. As in any democracy, what we eventually get will be exactly what we deserve.

THE LANDSCAPE

Part One

WHEN IDEOLOGIES COLLIDE

We Will Bury You

It was a cold morning in Moscow as twelve delegates from the countries of Eastern Europe sat down for their meeting. The date was November 9, 1989, and they had come to put the finishing touches to their latest five-year economic plan. Unbeknownst to them, 600 kilometres away in Germany, a series of events had already begun that would make their day's work completely irrelevant. The fall of the Berlin Wall later that afternoon ended 100 years of the world's greatest experiment in social restructuring.

COMECON, or the Council for Mutual Economic Aid, as it was officially known, had been formed after the Second World War by the Soviet Union to coordinate international trade among the communist countries in accordance with socialist principles. As such, it set quotas and prices for most goods according to the political priorities of the individual governments. Of course, the prices it set had little to do with actual market values of the goods, so it was difficult for the member states to conduct trade except through bilateral agreements at the intergovernmental level or by using barter.

COMECON had one other function, which was to stand in sharp ideological contrast to Western Europe's method of private enterprise and market-based pricing. In effect, it was making the statement "we can do better with our system than you can with your free market." The words "We will bury you," uttered at the United Nations in 1961 by Nikita Khrushchev as he took off his famous shoe and banged it on the table in front of the cameras, became widely quoted in the Western press. Those few words said it all. Khrushchev was referring to the contest between the free market capitalist system of the West and the regulated system of the COMECON countries, in which markets were forced to cooperate with the planned social objectives of the state. His prophecy failed to come to pass. The fall of the Wall ended more than COMECON itself. It also exposed, to the rest of the world, the amount of misery the system had created for those it tried to serve. Most significant of all, it shattered the century-long dream that economic laws could be forced to serve social and political interests.

Shattered in Eastern Europe, perhaps, but not in Canada. Over a decade later and in a different hemisphere, Canada still faces its own COMECON in the form of the Canada Health Act, and is approaching its own Berlin Wall in the impending collapse of its 'public only' health-care system.

How could things have gone so wrong? How could so many people, with the most deeply held humanitarian motivations, have destroyed the very objectives they were trying to save? Perhaps it is the classic human dilemma: when faced with a choice between our dreams and reality, which do we take? We are allowed to tantalize ourselves for a while—but in the end, history ensures that reality wins every time.

Not everyone will accept my analogy between the Berlin Wall and our cherished Canadian health-care system. Communism, for many North Americans, was just another brutal regime waiting to be overthrown. By contrast, Canadian health care looks like goodness incarnate.

But we remember the brutality of communism only because most of us are too young to recall its idealistic beginnings. Eighty years after it began, few remember that the Marxist states were originally founded on a resolution to eliminate poverty and elitism, help the disadvantaged and glorify the common man. Much like Canadian medicare, they racked up some impressive successes before the damage they caused managed to catch up with them.

This still leaves the problem of explaining why something with such good intentions is running into so much trouble. If the wall really *is* beginning to crumble, should we reinforce and defend it, or should we choose the opposite tactic and hasten its overthrow? Much like the East Germans during the late 1980s, Canadians are torn between the passions of those who remain committed to defending the existing system and those who want to abandon it. If an East German had been asked to choose whether to defend his system of government—as exemplified by the Wall—or to destroy it and opt for the unknown, which would he have chosen?

The answer would depend on who we chose to ask, but more important, *when* we chose to ask the question. Fifty years ago, the response would have been quite different from what we would have heard in the summer of 1989. Even at the time of the collapse, some citizens of the Eastern Bloc fervently believed they were the righteous defenders of humanitarian principles and that those in the West were agents of capitalist corruption.

Where, in this spectrum of shifting allegiance, would Canadians sit? Unlike the East Germans, we at least still have free speech (even if somewhat constrained by political correctness), so it is easier to tell in Canada where public opinion sits. Our polls tell us that health care is still one of the most passionately supported of Canadian values, but the percentage of people who defend the 'public only' aspect of our system decreases each year. Canadians have yet to wage the final battle in the war on this issue. About half of our population still wants to fight against what they see as the menace of 'two-tiered' health care. Do we have a wall? Not exactly a physical wall, of course, but we do have serious constraints—both practical and financial—that work to keep us inside the moral circle defined as 'Canadian' health care. Our federal politicians threaten funding cuts to punish provinces that step outside the 'public-only' wall they have built, even if they themselves person-ally find alternatives that sidestep the queues others must endure. The consequences of remaining faithful to the dream are more than a matter of convenience. For many waiting for cancer diag-nosis and treatment, they are a matter of life and death. Our wall is not a physical one, but a wall of fear. In order to do its job of keeping us inside, that fear must be constantly augmented and kept higher than our natural fear of illness and death.

"But Canada is different," some people will say. "We live in a democracy and we get to vote." Yes, we can vote, and our votes can change the people in charge. But some people seem to think we can choose from a wish list, and that the plurality of the vote in itself makes that choice right. Our vote can select a system, but whether it works or not is something we can only know by waiting. Or we can try to learn from the experience of others. Much like the choices the East Germans faced during the 1980s, our options are either to build the 'wall' higher or to tear it down and replace it with something else. The consequences, either way, will be ours to bear and will not be something we can simply vote out of existence.

The science that tries to predict the consequences of what we do is economics, and before we delve into more history, it is time for a very short lesson.

Creating Shortages: Economics at Work

What does economics have to do with health care? The simple answer is *everything*. The immediate threat to medicare in Canada is mediated by the threat of financial collapse, which in turn is the product of a set of false economic assumptions. These were built deep within the framework of the system that our leaders originally designed for us.

Comprehending why Canadian medicare has come to this point will require a little knowledge of some basic economic principles, and also an understanding of where shortages come from and how they feed the spiral of economic damage. Once in place, shortages consume the time of both management and staff, diverting them from more productive activities. They inflate the cost of manpower, cripple productivity, and make any attempt at disciplining employees a joke. In short, they cause an explosion of costs as industries struggle to compensate. Shortages are one of the most devastating—but also one of the least understood—of economic entities, and with good reason.

It is because there are two large and completely different schools of economics in the world. In many ways, the history of the twentieth century has been a staging ground for these two competing visions of how the laws of economics operate and how they can be made to work for us. As in everything, there are winners and there are losers. The stakes are large, literally involving the economies of entire nations. Compared to these large-scale conflicts, the health needs of a relatively well-to-do country of only 30 million inhabitants seem of minor consequence. But the fortunes of our health-care system ride on the results of the greatest economic experiment of the last century. It is only right that we take the time to learn a little of what recent history has to teach us.

"BMW fine—Trabi destroyed"

The headline is taken from an article dated November 14, 1989 in the *Höchster Kreisblatt*, a German newspaper, shortly after the Wall fell and the roads between the two Germanies became open. Date-lined in Frankfurt, it details the events surrounding the first face-to-face meeting between the East German Trabi automobile (short for Trabant) and the Western equivalent.[1]

Frankfurt (fh). The first accident involving a Trabi in Frank-furt had unusual results. A 27-year-old from Apolda near Erfurt and his 19-year-old girlfriend crossed the Friedens-brücke in the Sachsenhausen direction and stopped too late, crashing into a BMW from Langen. Although the impact was heavy, the Western bumper took it undamaged.

The Trabi, on the other hand, wasn't made for such a kind of rendezvous. "Absolutely ripe for the scrap heap," concluded the police. But instead of two arguing people, a crowd met the police. Lots of passing drivers had stopped to help. An elderly man pre-sented the couple with 50 DM, and a policeman invited them to stay at his home for the night, which they thankfully accepted. One man offered to take the Trabi to the border, but the police declined because it was damaged beyond repair.

The young couple had their Trabi delivered home nevertheless, hoping to find someone to repair it at home. The small damage to the BMW bumper bar will be paid for by an insurance association.

East meets West. A classic theme, and a symbolic event for the German audience considering the times. The specific analogy is the

---

[1] Taken from http://www.remote.org/frederik/culture/berlin/hk-14-11-03.html, posted by Frederik Ramm.

controlled market system of Eastern Europe colliding with the free market system of the West. The message seems clear enough. When no direct comparisons are allowed, the Eastern system appears adequate, but when the wall opens and a true comparison is allowed to happen, we can see for ourselves which system is the better and which will prevail.

But to many, the message seems counterintuitive. How can the free market system, with its risk of chaos, really be superior to the orderly, planned, giant economies of the socialist countries? Why does the Trabi—the symbol of the old Honecker regime—get demolished, while its rival the BMW—the symbol of Western affluence—barely gets scratched? The answers to these questions lie in the way each system thinks of "*market*." Socialist economics treats the *market* as a wild monster that needs to be tamed. This is because markets, according to this way of thinking, harm normal people by allowing a small minority to cash in on the misery of others. The job of taming the market monster understandably requires tremendous power and resources, hence the task falls to a government.

Failed attempts to tame the market were usually attributed to inadequate resources, or the difficulty controlling enough of the economy at the same time. There appeared to be a critical mass effect as far as the job of market-taming was concerned. If you tried to do it in too small a community, it was bound to fail because of the spillover from adjacent market economies that eluded the mechanism of control. Hence, the gigantic economies of the Soviet Union—and the reason why this was the world's greatest social experiment. Finally, with the creation of the USSR, the scale of the operation was elevated to a level never seen before. This time it had to work.

Many Canadians still distrust markets. The word itself is often used as a synonym for evil, or at least for a level of unpredictability that approaches chaos. A significant number subscribe to the notion that markets are malicious forces that need to be tamed.

Most tolerate markets for providing them with consumer items and other things that seem less important, but try telling a Canadian that allowing a market to operate without intervention will improve health care and you are asking for a fight. Health care is something that Canadians feel is "too important" to be left to the uncertainties of a market.

What is ironic is that Canadians vigorously defended the principle of market competition when it involved the imminent break-up of a national airline. They feared the resulting monopoly if only one major air carrier were left to service all of the important air routes in the country. They voiced loudly their concern that a monopoly would mean a rise in airfares and a drop in the quality of service. They understood that a loss of choice would leave them helpless against the whims of the only supplier. Yet those same people (quite literally often the same people) are prepared to go to the mats to fight to maintain the largest government-supported monopoly in the country, their health-care system. They demonstrate in front of legislature buildings, and mount passionate campaigns equating anyone opposing their views with fascists trying to tear apart the fabric of Canada, all to prevent any competitive market forces from exerting their effect. All to prevent Canadians from having an alternative choice to the current monopoly in health care.

Ignoring the market in the finance or clothing industries is one thing. But in the case of health care, the market happens to be sick people—and ignoring the market means ignoring whether their medical needs are met. The tangible result is longer lineups for everything from family doctors to heart surgery. The other side of the same market consists of the providers. Ignoring that side of the market means failing to provide adequate staff and equipment to care for the sick. The long waits in Canada for hospital beds, surgeries, and nursing home placements is a direct result of our historic mistrust of markets and market forces. But if that is all that resulted—if it were only longer waits than we would like and less technology than we would like—that might not be so bad. The most insidious and destructive aspect of the government-controlled monopoly, which is central to the socialist economic model, is something else. It is the continual fuelling of a process that creates shortages, a process that gathers increasing momentum over time and cannot stop.

Many people still think of the current shortages in health care workers as random events like floods or famine, things that are admittedly onerous but simply need to be weathered out until the tide turns and improvement takes place. They act as if most of the problems will disappear on their own if we only have the fortitude to stick it out until things improve. Some see them as unforeseen errors accidentally created along the way which may need to be rectified, but can be corrected by minor adjustments. These people feel we are overall on the right track with our medicare system, but that fine-tuning is required, or perhaps some better management strategies must be found before we can achieve our goal. Some argue that our system achieves a lot, in spite of inevitable imperfections, and still serves the overall interest of the majority quite well most of the time. These people believe that no system is perfect and that some shortcomings are inevitable. They argue that our shortcomings are preferred over those of, say, the Americans.

But if the dislocations are fundamental to our own processes and not random events, then we must know this—because, in that case, the tide will never 'turn' on its own and the problems will never improve unless we change the offending processes. If this is the case, and if we remain unprepared to re-examine these fundamentals, we will never achieve the health-care goals we have set for ourselves. On the contrary, things will just continue to get worse until they completely break down, or until people have had enough.

Many people still reject this notion out of hand, believing the very nobility of our objectives somehow protects us from having made this kind of error. This prospect is so serious that even those who are convinced we are on the right track should be prepared to at least go through the examination, because the result of not doing so would be a death sentence to the very ideals they hold.

In this chapter I will argue that this is in fact the case: that our fundamental principles have laid the ground for long-term economic disaster. The early apparent success of medicare was precisely that—an early result that took advantage of some initial opportunities at the expense of long-term consequences. The processes we have used were inherently "creators of shortages," and in the long run, these shortages are forming a garrotte which threatens to choke the last breath from the system.

These are expansive statements, but an understanding of shortages and how they work is essential if one is to understand the way out of our current health care crisis. A little patience is required while we digress for a brief visit into the world of economics.

The Shortage is King

In conventional economics, shortages are defined in *relative* terms. The concept of a shortage, in other words, only has meaning when compared to the demand for the same item. A shortage of any commodity—such as sugar, for example—means nothing in the absolute sense if we talk about the total number of tons of available sugar. It has meaning only when we talk of a shortage *relative to the demand* for sugar. This is in stark contrast to the socialist view of supply, which prefers to measure in absolute terms. COMECON would have measured sugar in kilograms as an absolute quantity or number. They might have compared that number to the quantity they had set as a target or quota. This same quantity is often euphemistically referred to as the "need," which sounds better than a quota even though it is established the same way. But to compare it to actual *demand* was unthinkable, because consumer demand within the socialist definition of economics had no meaning. Consumers were simply supposed to do what they were told. In the Western system, demand is all-important, because the same quantity of sugar that today is a shortage may turn into a glut if the demand suddenly falls—as when, for example, a healthier substitute becomes available instead.

In a free market, true shortages cannot occur, because price fluctuations auto-regulate demand. That is to say, when the supply of sugar fails to meet the demand, the price goes up, eliminating some of the demand. The immediate humanitarian response is "*but then some people are going to go without sugar.*" This would be true if the amount of sugar people needed were fixed. It would also be true if people had no discretion in the way they chose to spend their money. For example, as long as people could afford the increased price of sugar by postponing their holiday to Hawaii, or by purchasing a less-expensive car, they would not be going without sugar unless they chose to do so.

More importantly, the rise in the price of sugar acts as a signal to those in the sugar-producing business to increase both the price and the supply. In the short term, some people may truly go without sugar—but in the longer term, sugar production rises because of increased investment which follows the increased potential for profit. In other words, the price of sugar *appears* to go up as the demand rises, and later tends to fall back. Transient shortages, therefore, have an important function, because they act as an indicator of where people should invest their money and time.

The consumer side of the equation is equally important. Price, seen by some people as merely a barrier to access, is much more than that—it is a carrier of information. When there is a choice between products with different prices, there is a natural motivation to choose the lower price (assuming the other factors are equal). These are automatic activities built into any market. So, the trio relationship between supply, demand, and price acts to stabilize and regulate the supply of sugar and influence the consumer's choice about purchase.

The effect of availability on price and the feedback to increase supply has been well demonstrated in a public way in the worldwide market for oil. The term "market efficiency" refers to how quickly a particular market responds to changes in one or more of these parameters. One of the most efficient markets in the world, for example, is the international market for currency exchange. The more encumbered a market is with regulation or the more difficult it is for information to pass freely, the less efficient the market becomes, because it takes a long time for regulations to allow the necessary changes to take place.

Partial intervention in markets is almost everywhere in our economy. We have marketing boards to regulate supply in our agricultural products, tariff commissions to control exports and imports, and the CRTC to control what we watch on our television sets. In most cases, we allow some market activity, but only under strict supervision. For most of the goods in our economy, we still allow markets to set prices, we allow freedom of choice for consumers, and we allow private initiative to operate within the limits we proscribe. But nowhere is the disavowal of anything resembling a market more complete than in our Canadian health-care system. When health care is at stake, our laws specifically prohibit any prices, any competition, and consequently any choice on the part of the consumer. The result is a short-term bonanza for those who receive the benefit of low prices and unimpeded supply. The long-term result is the loss of all information about product quality and how money should be spent, and the creation of a self-perpetuating spiral of increasing shortages.

To understand how the disruption of natural market forces does its damage, we will go back to our example of the sugar market and ask what happens when an intervention is made with a humanitarian intent.

As we saw, no one likes to see people go without sugar, so the natural intervention when a shortage appears is to stabilize the price by law, preventing it from rising beyond the reach of those who might otherwise be left without. This satisfies the immediate need of those who might otherwise not be able to afford sugar, but what does it do for the incentive to produce more? The answer is nothing. In fact, in the long term it actually exacerbates the shortage, because it does nothing to encourage those using more sugar than they really need, to conserve. More insidious yet, any information carried by the price of sugar (such as where to get it for the least price, or when to consider switching to an alternative) is obliterated, or at least distorted to the point of being misleading.

At some point, the relative shortage of sugar worsens, rekindling the same scenario all over again. Each time the price is "stabilized" by external means, the foundations are laid for an even worse shortage on the next go-around. Intervention will fail, eventually, because price fixing is not and will never be a replacement for actual sugar. When this point is reached, the demand for sugar so far exceeds the supply that there simply is none, unless one resorts to a black market. Black (or illegal) markets actually perform a needed function here, by providing an alternative, and by quoting realistic (at least, unregulated) prices. Because the shortage opens the way for exorbitant profits, those in control move their product from legitimate markets, where the price is low, to illegal markets, where the price is uncontrolled. As sure as there are shortages, black markets will appear, taking advantage of the price rise, but also filling in the need to those who can afford to pay.

The best place to study shortages was in the Soviet Union, or one of the other Eastern European countries dominated by a communist economy. Although much of the lesson has been erased since the fall of communism, the aftermath is still easily seen and it is not difficult to find people willing to discuss the region's recent economic history. By the end of the 1980s, the effects of bureaucratically-controlled prices had reached their peak. The evidence that things had reached a limit could be seen in four major ways:

- *True shortages*
- *Lack of investment causing infrastructure collapse*
- *A thriving underground industry of black markets*
- *Introduction of "Dollar Stores"*

TRUE SHORTAGES

Moscow in the late 1980s was a city rife with shortages. It was a place where the official price of bread was only two rubles (the equivalent then of about half a cent) if you could find any, but the government stores were all sold out by 9 a.m. every day. Bread was always available if you knew someone, but the going rate on that market was closer to 25 rubles. Once the "free market" was allowed to operate in the heart of Moscow, in 1988, under the new rules of *glasnost*, bread became freely available there for those who cared to pay for only 15 rubles, undercutting the black market price, but still much higher than the 2-ruble price in the government stores where bread was usually simply not available. For ordinary Russians, the shock was a dramatic one, but the story is not complete until we know that the "world price" for bread—that is, in most other countries—was the equivalent of about 60 rubles, or about two dollars Canadian (depending on how one valued the Russian currency, but that is a different story). So, a 15-ruble price was still cheap for foreign visitors, but seemed exorbitant to Muscovites who were still comparing costs to the "official" prices. What they failed to appreciate was how long they had been protected from world prices before the system failed to work at all.

Bread and sugar are only illustrations, of course. The shortages in Moscow included almost all commodities—especially money—but more particularly goods such as pharmaceuticals, and medical equipment which could not be produced within Russia and had to be imported.

LACK OF INVESTMENT

The fact that bread had to be sold on the official market at only two rubles per loaf may have had something to do with the lack of investment in bakeries and granaries. In Russia, only the state was allowed to make these investments, and this policy seemed to work as long as the state could do so. But it could not go on forever. State funding eventually reaches an endpoint, as long as the state is not interested in making a profit and the funds it invests are always subsidies.

The lack of investment in bakeries was only the tip of the iceberg, of course. The same principles applied to other public investments. When buildings or systems started to fall apart, there was no money for repairs or to replace old or obsolete equipment. The problem was not that apparent if you never left Moscow. For anyone visiting from the outside and familiar with conditions elsewhere, however, Moscow became a city of despair, with signs of poverty at every turn.

BLACK MARKETS

Governments tend to think their laws apply to everyone, but there is a significant element in every population that feels otherwise. For these people, rules are for the helpless, not for them. They believe in their own ability to help themselves, and their experience generally supports their personal convictions. Most of the time they do get away with breaking rules, and often the profits are substantial. The shortages created by government price fixing provide golden opportunities for these people to fill a need that is not met by anyone else.

Typically, black markets are highly efficient, but also volatile because of the lack of controls. The price of bread on this market might be affected by anything from competition from other black market operators, to a restriction of supply because gangland killings have disrupted the supply chain. It is the kind of market that polite company likes to pretend does not exist—but the reality is that it *does* exist, and commands a significant share of any economy. One way to provide extra opportunities for those in black market operations is to create shortages. One might go so far as to say that shortages are for black markets what blood in the sea is for sharks.

An excellent example within our own history can be found in the Prohibition era. The ban on alcohol sales in the U.S. was a virtual gold mine for organized crime. Billions of dollars changed hands as the price for alcohol was buoyed upwards by the ban on legal sales, until the repeal of the prohibition laws in 1933 finally ended the frenzy.

One absolutely critical point needs to be made about black markets. The very name suggests a dark, sinister activity that lies outside the law and cannot be tolerated. We are, for the most part, a law-abiding people that have built a society on the principles of orderliness, and we cherish structure and predictability. The natural reaction to black market or any other illicit activity is, therefore, to stamp it out. Those who try are in for a painful lesson, because black market activity is an animal that feeds on shortages at the same time as it provides an avenue for relieving the very shortages on which it thrives.

Trying to suppress black market activity, therefore, is like trying to put out a fire with gasoline. It merely feeds the cycle by further aggravating the shortage underlying the problem in the first place. Even worse, it harms those in search of the desired goods or services by making them more scarce and expensive. The process is driven by governments who fall prey to the illusion that more vigorous enforcement is a solution instead of understanding their own role in pushing the cycle.

So, far from being all bad, black markets can be useful—first, to tell us when a shortage exists, and second, to service at least some of the people suffering from that shortage. A third use of black markets is something outsiders instantly see, while people who live within the system rarely do. That is the information they provide about what things really cost. While bread was in short supply in Moscow at the official price, it was readily available on the free market at very close to the black market price. Perhaps the best example was the price in Moscow of one of the scarcest commodities—money itself, as evident in the exchange rate between the dollar and ruble. (The term 'hard currency' was routinely used to denote any of the freely convertible currencies, as exemplified by the dollar. By implication, the ruble and anything else that was not freely convertible was not considered real money.)

By mid-1989, the official value of the ruble—pegged at 1.4 to the American dollar—was widely regarded as a joke, and used only in large barter transactions with other COMECON countries. Tourists exchanged only as much money at the official rate as they were forced to, relying on the many tour guides and hotel staff that would gladly give up to 10 rubles for a coveted American dollar, or any other western currency for that matter, that could be freely converted. By 1989, the Russian government was forced to acknowledge the loss of revenue and adopted a 'tourist rate' of six rubles to the American dollar, available only to tourists, while they continued to insist that the 'official rate' of 1.4 still stood. The new rate was successful in increasing revenues of foreign currency by government, by making it less worthwhile to take a risk on black market trading, although much illicit trading continued. Successful, that is, for a short while, as the black market rate continued to soar beyond what the government was prepared to accept.

By 1992, as the rate soared to over 500 rubles to the dollar, the pretense could no longer be maintained. The government gave up trying to control the value of their own money. Currency restrictions in Russia were finally lifted in 1993, as the Russian economy continued its tailspin, with the ruble soaring over 1000 to the dollar. By the end of 1995, the ruble was trading at 4,600 to the U.S. dollar, and still showed no sign of stopping—reaching 6,000 rubles to the dollar by the end of 1997, when the Russian government issued new currency re-valued at one new ruble for 1,000 old rubles. The new denominations fooled no one, however—the 1998 ruble, starting off at six new rubles to the dollar, has continued to erode. Its current value of 32 rubles to one U.S. dollar, at the end of 2002, is roughly 1/5,000th its value ten years earlier.

It was a startling string of events, showing that in the face of a shortage (in this case of 'hard' currency) even a major national government was powerless and far from helping, price controls merely accelerated the existing shortage. If the black market itself seemed bizarre, it was only a prelude to one of the more pathetic and ironic of all economic activities.

DOLLAR STORES

These form a bizarre sort of hybrid enterprise that usually indicates an advanced state of economic breakdown. Anyone who visited one of the Eastern European countries just before the fall of communism will know what they are.

> *Picture a winter scene in the heart of Moscow. A native Muscovite huddles in his thin, worn coat to keep warm as he gazes longingly through the brightly lit window filled with goods he*

can only dream about. The store counters are filled with tins of ham, bottles of olive oil, coats and hats, and the best vodka the country could produce. It is not just the price he cannot hope to afford. As a native Russian, he is not allowed into the store, period. This is a "dollar store," so-called because the only currency accepted there is the American dollar (or any Western currency freely convertible into American dollars). Russian citizens are by law forbidden to carry foreign currency (except diplomats or others who can show a reason for having it for official business). Prior to 1992, Russians caught carrying foreign currency were punished by jail terms. That meant only tourists could enter the store, where they were encouraged to spend their western currency on Russian goods. Payment in rubles inside the store by anyone (foreign or otherwise) was always politely refused.

How is it that, in the very heart of a country founded on the most humanitarian of principles, the glorification of the worker, and the building of a classless society, such an insult could occur? A citizen barred from entering a store in his own city, kept from access to goods reserved for only foreign visitors with real money?

The answer is that the shortages had created a huge source of potential revenue for the state itself, selling to the only people left who could still afford them—namely, foreign visitors. Goods that were still scarce for ordinary Russians suddenly became available at the right price. It was a matter of the black market becoming so lucrative that even government could not ignore the opportunity to jump in and make a profit—a classic example of the old maxim, *"If you can't beat 'em, join 'em."*

Dollar stores disappeared from Russia immediately once the currency restrictions were lifted in the early 1990s. So did the black markets and the exorbitant profits made on currency exchange. As soon as the value of the ruble was allowed to float, currency trading and the carrying of foreign currency were no longer illegal. They did not have to be, since that segment of the black market had lost its appeal.

How Does COMECON Fit into the Picture?

COMECON was formed in the post-war period to deal with the economies of the satellite countries of the Soviet Union. Prior to the war, all economic policy came directly from the Kremlin and was carried out without much consultation, since the entire country was under direct rule. The advent of the satellite countries made it necessary to have a vehicle to ensure Soviet-dominated nations continued to govern their trading relations according to the rules of socialist philosophy.

It was COMECON, therefore, that determined what each participating country or region would need in the way of food, clothing, and all other commodities, and also from where (within the Soviet bloc countries) those could be most easily produced. Since it concerned itself only with production inside countries all with a common philosophy, it deliberately ignored the issue of currency and any value it might have had. In the world of COMECON, politics was a higher authority than money, which was simply seen as a vehicle to carry out the trades sanctioned by the group. It was a world in which the 'value' (as we would know it) of various goods was not of concern or was assigned arbitrarily, debts were routinely forgiven, and money was treated the way large retail stores might handle their own coupons or vouchers. It was not unlike a large trade-by-barter agency that ignored the outside world and its monetary rules, relying on the sheer size of the trading bloc to supply anything that was needed.

For many years, it appeared to succeed. In the longer term, however, the damage caused by ignoring the economic rules of the rest of the world caught up with the Soviets and destroyed their economy. Put in a nutshell, the naïve attitude toward money laid the foundation for financial collapse, the lack of financial incentives destroyed industrial capacity, and the lack of a market that was allowed to define 'need' created widespread poverty.

What Does This Have to Do With Canadian Health Care?

Some may already have guessed the parallel between the Soviet-type economy and our version, resident in our health system. In Canada, the "market" for health care is composed of individuals who need something the health-care system has to offer, on the one side, and those with the means to provide that care on the other. Our COMECON consists of government ministries that decide how much of what is needed and where resources should go. True to the model, this is done in absolute rather than relative terms, with finite dollar values fixing the quantities of care that have been calculated to meet the 'need.' The concept of demand is not acknowledged except as a force to be resisted. The "shortages" are manifested in hospital deficits and difficulty finding people with the needed skills willing to work. The theoretical shortages turn suddenly to stark reality for those people stuck in jammed emergency rooms. They come home to us in the prolonged waits that we tolerate, even when these waits exceed all reasonable parameters, and even when they are dangerous to our health. The "cost" is something we know little about, because it is buried within our government financial statements, but we hear that there is little accountability except at the end of the year, when the budget faces us. Our politicians and economists reassure us with the news that the total cost of health care in Canada is low relative to what is spent in the U.S. Low prices were also a feature of the commodities such as food and clothing supposedly available in official Soviet stores. The 'black markets' are evident in the many ways Canadians avoid the harmful aspects of the system—whether that is an over-reliance on emergency departments, abuses of privilege by doctors, nurses, politicians, and professional athletes, or simply those who can afford not to wait and seek care in the United States. As with any black market, there are no reliable statistics on the extent to which people bend the rules to protect their own interests.

In fact, medicare in Canada has followed the economic principles of the old Soviet regime almost perfectly. The *Canada Health Act* forbids alternate sources of health care (at least as far as hospitals are concerned) other than those provided by government, paralleling the Russian laws against carrying foreign currency (after all, the only real value of foreign currency was the ability to buy things outside of Russian control). Thankfully in our case, the restrictions (and therefore the damage) are confined to health care instead of being applied to the entire economy.

The painful lesson is that shortages, once they occur, are extremely expensive things to reverse, and often well outside the bounds of what governments can manage with legislation and price controls. Short-term victories can be won, of course, but the long-term winner is never in doubt. The law of supply and demand will always rule in the end, and it is for this reason that the shortage is always king.

It is interesting that the same concern for protecting the public does not seem to extend to airline travel. In 1996, with a minimum of fanfare, the Canadian government introduced legislation taking the responsibility for maintaining safety in air traffic control away from its own Ministry of Transport, and giving it to a private company called *Nav Canada*. In a curious exchange of roles, it is now the Americans who are experiencing horrendous organizational problems with their federal system (FAA) of air traffic control, and they are most intrigued with the free-market style Canadian solution. Before *Nav Canada* was in place, Canadian air traffic control system had suffered many of the same problems that now plague the U.S. system: its equipment was antiquated, and a proposed replacement was behind schedule and far over budget. Since then, *Nav Canada* has managed to reduce air traffic delays, cut costs, and revamp its technology. What a switch! In air traffic control, it is the Americans who are stuck with a public system that is not working, and it is they who are jealously eyeing the Canadian solution: harnessing private initiative.

If a public-private partnership works so well in air traffic control, one wonders why health care must conform to a public-only agenda. It might not matter so much if a less important segment of our economy had been targeted. But after only 30 years of such control, all ostensibly for our own good, and all for apparently humanitarian reasons, we have finally reached all the features so familiar to those who lived through the communist eras in Russia. The last signpost on the way to financial collapse are dollar stores, and their equivalent is just starting to take shape in Canada as cash-starved hospitals eagerly eye the potential revenue that services restricted only to foreign citizens would bring. It is not quite here yet in health care, although the phenomenon has already surfaced in many of our universities and public schools, which have begun to charge exorbitant fees (by Canadian standards) for seats restricted to foreign students. The final saga, the financial death-knell of public systems, must be lurking just around the corner. When the equivalent of the 'dollar store' comes to health care, we will know the end is finally near.

Effects of Shortages I: The Illusions

The major components of the labour sector in health care are doctors, hospitals, nurses, and other technical support workers (technicians who work in labs, x-ray, respiratory and cardiology services, ambulances, etc.). Manpower shortages are now a serious problem in all of these groups.

We hear there are more doctors in Canada than ever before. Using the old Soviet method of absolute numbers and allotments, there is no doctor shortage in Canada. But in a market-based system, shortages are *relative* to need. Much press has been devoted to the tendency of Canadians to abuse their "free" access to doctors under medicare and the need to control this as a way of preventing unreasonable cost increases. Although there is some truth to this, there are also legitimate reasons for an increased demand for doctors. Some of the indisputable factors that have *increased* our need for doctors relative to the past are:

- Technology—there are simply more things that can be done and most Canadians want current level technology when they have cancer or a heart attack—not that which was available thirty years ago.

- We have more people. The census in 1970 was 21 million, and today is almost 31 million (source: *Statistics Canada*).

- We have an older population, with a consequently higher rate of illness, requiring more care. In 1970, the average age of Canadians was 26.4; by the end of 2002 it was nearly 36.5 (source: *Statistics Canada*). More than 21 percent of all Canadians were over 50 years of age in the year 2000.

- More of the care we now provide is in-hospital, is more intensive, and requires more specialist physicians, than in the past.

- Our increased ability to travel and communicate leads us to expect remote communities to have similar levels of care to those in larger centres.

At the same time as the *need* for physicians has gone up, the *supply* has gone down:

For many years, governments attempting to control their medicare costs have noticed what appeared to be a linear relationship between the number of practicing doctors and the total costs for medical care. The consensus among health-care economists in Canada has tended to reinforce what politicians wanted to hear—that more doctors meant more costs, without any obvious and measurable improvement in health. Never mind that there were no accepted measurements for health outcomes, and the advisors used nothing more complex than death rates and life expectancy as a measure of health.

Death rates result from a multitude of variables besides effective health care. They are a useful way to measure health care in Third World countries or under conditions of abject poverty, but are hopelessly insensitive to policy changes within healthy modern economies. Even if they were sensitive to these changes, imagine waiting for death rates to tell us if a new policy were effective or not. It would take several years and thousands of dead Canadians before we could tell something wasn't working, several more years to agree what that cause was, and then multiple years of policy changes to effectively turn it around. By that time, the demographic and technological changes would have made the original data irrelevant. There is no way to monitor health effectiveness in a modern context by simply following death rates.

Nevertheless, politicians are only human, and a message one wants to hear is always to be preferred over the alternative. Under a series of measures, and following the Barer-Stoddard report in the mid 1980s, medical school enrollments were slashed in 1993 by ten percent across Canada. Because of the time it takes medical students to become real doctors, the effect of that disastrous policy move only began to be felt at the end of the century. Even greater reductions to the "effective" physician supply resulted from the following additional policies:

1. The lengthening of the medical "internship" necessary to become licensed increased across Canada to two years from one (1993/94). This was achieved without a corresponding increase in students or funding for intern/residency positions, and meant one full year in which no new doctors graduated.

2. Fee capping and limits to negotiated settlements that failed to keep up with the overhead costs of running a practice convinced many Canadian physicians to leave the country or fall back on other ways of generating income (consulting, holistic medicine, diet medicine) that were not restricted by government. Familiar methods of limiting the dollars available to doctors included a restriction on new billing numbers and a collusive agreement between the medical association in BC and that provincial government to limit earnings of new physicians to 50 percent of the fee schedule (this was eventually overturned by a legal challenge). Other provinces followed similar methods at various times to limit the attractiveness of their province to new doctors.

3. Limitations on operating room time and hospital beds where costs generally explode, have long been used as a natural bottleneck to prevent patients from getting into the hospital. This has the same effect as a decrease in pay, since many physicians derive most of their income from doing in-hospital surgical procedures. In the meantime, surgeons still have to be available on-call—time which they had traditionally provided for free on the understanding that access to operating room time would be forthcoming. This is why many surgeons now are demanding to be paid for on-call time, in addition to the more usual methods of fees for providing a procedural service. As

they watch their access to operating rooms disappear, they wonder who changed the deal.

4. A higher proportion of our doctors are going into specialties. Although this leaves the total count the same, shortages in specific fields become more evident since doctors rarely work in specialties in which they were not trained.

5. A higher proportion of doctors now entering the workforce are women, many of whom want to balance family with their careers, providing less than 100-percent full-time equivalent practitioners, but still occupying a full seat in medical school. Women bring a fresh and much-needed perspective to the medical profession, but no one wants to do the arithmetic.

6. Women are not the only ones choosing a different mix of personal and professional life. Newer medical graduates of both genders are less likely to accept the 80-hour workweeks and gruelling schedules that were once a normal part of training and practice for a previous generation of physicians. This is evident in the refusal of PARI (the Professional Association of Residents and Interns, representing new doctors doing in-hospital training) to accept more than one day in four on-call (previously a one-in-two call was not unusual on some services). Whatever one thinks of the new expectations, the effect is less service unless compensated by an increase in manpower, which is simply not there.

7. Pay for university appointments—once an attraction and a source of prestige for physicians—has fallen well below the standards needed to keep successful teachers and researchers. Canadian universities now rely too much on funding for clinical work to provide an adequate financial incentive, and are asking their faculty to do more and more of their teaching *pro-bono*.

For all these reasons, a simple measure of the "number of doctors" in the country has lost its meaning, yet we still see it quoted. The shortage is not limited to doctors. Nursing shortages have received much press lately. Most hospitals have increasing trouble recruiting the staff they need, and are forced to pay overtime rates in order to meet even minimum staffing standards. In many hospitals, technician shortages cause service cancellations even when physicians are in place and ready to proceed. Last year, the hospitals near Vancouver saw decreases as high as 15 percent in the number of inpatient service days they were providing in only *ONE* year, and the rate of decrease is rising. Such a decrease might sound like a successful cost-saving measure, except that the decrease in services actually *cost more* to provide—the changes were unpredictable, and resulted from nursing shortages that required an increase in the use of overtime rates. At the same time as costs went up and service went down, emergency ward congestion and surgical cancellations increased, again due to the unpredictable nature of nursing staff shortages.

Perhaps more important than the actual shortages themselves, there is absolutely no relief in sight and things are only expected to get worse. Decades of policies that underpaid for services cannot be quickly turned around. Efforts to increase the supply of nursing staff pay off very slowly and tend to continually underestimate the size of the shortage. Moreover, efforts to recruit nurses generally fail to acknowledge the role that price intervention has played in creating the shortage in the first place. Payment for any group of nurses, as in any collective bargaining process, is always based on the value of the previous contract negotiated between the nurses' union and government. The results of the bargaining process have become an excellent test in political skill and the resolve of each side in bettering their deal, but *have nothing to do with the market*. So, we have a system in which price is fixed by debating skills without any connection to the natural market forces of supply or demand.

As a result, hospitals are finding more and more difficulty getting the nurses they have to work the extra hours required to make up for the shortage. Older nurses are becoming increasingly intolerant and are simply saying 'no' when asked to come in for work. They are demanding and getting more and more of their time compensated at overtime rates. Some have learned that, by waiting until the hospital is desperate, they can receive overtime pay instead of straight time. Why should they work for straight time when time-and-a-half or even double-time is easy to get?

Instead of recognizing the role salary scales play in the shortage of nurses and raising pay to attract more of them, hospitals in some provinces have actually done the reverse and agreed among themselves not to raise rates above the negotiated amounts. They know it would otherwise force the other hospitals to raise their rates also to keep from losing their staff. They do this, of course, because they have no assurance added costs can be recouped from government. Ignoring for the moment that this kind of wage collusion would be illegal in any other industry, they seem not to realize that their actions lock them further into the same policies that created the shortage in the first place.

Shortages, once established, give all the power to those with the skills or products in demand. The major benefactors (not necessarily of their own making) are the professional associations and unions that are now in the enviable position of controlling an increasingly scarce resource.

Effects of shortages II: Power, Price, and Black Markets

An examination of the power structures that determine direction in health care today shows why there is little chance for significant change. The shortages all play into the hands of the players at the table who control the supply of people and money.

THE PROVIDERS AND UNIONS

All the unions involved in health care—including provincial medical associations which form the bargaining units for doctors, nurses' unions, technicians' unions and the hospital employees' unions—benefit from shortages, because they are in control of the processes that allow people to work in their respective jobs. A heightened demand for their people gives them the upper hand in their bargaining positions. All of them have resisted suggestions to lower the barriers to entry for new workers, citing as their reason the need to protect standards.

For example, the colleges that control physician licensing do not accept candidates with medical training from countries outside the commonwealth without rigorous review, re-examination, or re-training. While this may make sense for those trained in some Third World countries, the net includes much of the U.S., as well as countries such as Germany and France. In their zeal to defend standards, the colleges seem to forget the damage caused by the spiral of shortages to those same standards. The barriers are further reinforced by immigration laws, which still consider health-care professionals a drain on government resources instead of an asset.

To be fair, even those making a sincere attempt to reverse the trend find themselves hampered by current laws and previous practice. The College of Physicians & Surgeons of BC, for example, was recently fined $10 million for 'indirect discrimination' by a Human Rights tribunal for deciding a group of foreign physicians needed more training before being licensed to practice. The term acknowledges that they did not *intend* to discriminate, but fines were levied anyway since discrimination occurred. Their track record in granting licenses to other foreign physicians was not taken into consideration. Understandably, since no one is prepared to indemnify the association (which exists on private fees) for an adverse legal outcome, they have declared their unwillingness to even look at any more external candidates.

In general, however, all of the professional bodies benefit to one degree or another from the monopoly that government created being the sole health-care provider, through protected jobs and incomes, and freedom from concern about competition.

THE GOVERNMENTS

The desire of governments to lower costs by micromanaging the system has been a major cause in the first place of the shortages we now bear. A sudden reversal in this is unlikely to occur—partly because the same need to control costs is even more pressing than before, and partly because it would be an admission of previous mistakes. Some would argue that governments reject giving more power to consumers in the area of health care because they are hooked on the political prestige that comes with their traditional patriarchal role of provider. In other words, if people had the ability to make their own choices and look after their own health interests, the government would lose one of its major justifications for the size of its power base.

THE POWERLESS CONSUMER

It should be evident that all financial decisions relating to the quantity of health care available are made with only the first two groups at the table, and all of them have an interest—or at the very least, once had an interest—in keeping the supply of health-care providers limited. This historical fact guaranteed that, while the agreements reached may have been an effective test of the relative wills of these groups, they had little if anything to do with the "market." Therefore, the demand from thousands of Canadian consumers waiting patiently in line was essentially ignored.

It is a sad testament to our democratic system that the one group not allowed any representation (or any financial information, since the health-care costs are hopelessly buried within general revenue) has been the consumer. Although we are free to use the "black market" by accessing health care in the U.S., it is only after we have already paid our full share of the costs of Canadian health care through our taxes.

Lessons from History

It is time for a review of the economic lessons we can learn from history, and a review of how they might apply to health care in Canada. What is the '*Dominant Model*' of health care in Canada? Where did it come from and how will it end?

Many groups who protest our current system have predicted that it will collapse in an unworkable state. Perhaps so, but why has it not already done so? Many people want to know how the collapse will work because they want to be able to protect themselves from the fallout. There is no way to check any of the numerous predictions being made. The best we can do is to look at the lessons of history. How did other economic regimes fare that ignored market fundamentals? What triggered their eventual collapse and what lessons do they hold for us?

Again, the closest parallels lie within recent history in the fall of the economies of Eastern Europe and the Soviet Union. We do not quite yet have "dollar stores" for health care in Canada, although they are being talked about with increasing frequency. Most of our large hospitals can still offer world-class service at attractive rates for patients from other countries seeking elective surgery, and many have at least considered this option in their need to replace revenue lost from government funding. Although such a policy could be easily justified as a way of raising the revenue necessary to provide needed care to Canadians, the optics of admitting to a double system—with the upper end reserved for foreigners and the lower end for Canadians—is politically risky. But the "dollar store" equivalent materialized in Moscow quite late in the cycle, for the same reasons and just a few years prior to the economic collapse. In other words, the fact that dollar stores are politically risky does not prevent them from happening; it only delays them until we have reached a higher level of financial desperation. Perhaps this is a good sign and we can relax. If the Soviet lesson is anything to go by, the complete collapse of our Canadian health-care system will not come until *AFTER* our hospitals have begun marketing our health services to offshore clients for profit. Once that happens, complete collapse will follow very quickly.

The other element in Russia, prior to its economic collapse, was an active black market in both currencies and goods. Russian citizens, like Canadians, were powerless to reverse the political processes that shaped their country, but did have the ability to subvert the economic order in their own small corner by supporting the underworld economy. This was not, of course, an open choice, but a matter of necessity. The equivalent process in Canadian health care will be a rush for private services of all kinds, legal or not. While government may try to stifle the pioneers in private health care, their efforts only serve to increase the demand—and, consequently, the profit potential—for those willing to take the risk. Eventually, we will see a proliferation of clinics that are either completely private, or more likely, offer a blend of public and private services that are difficult to prevent or prosecute.

We are still early in this terminal stage of the process, but the more alternate services there are, the more public demand for them will grow, and the more they will pull trained staff (both physicians and others) away from the public services. We can expect increased resolve from our governments to stem the tide and crack down, but just as the illegal drug trade has proven beyond their grasp because their very efforts increase criminal profits, so will "choice medical care" increase the more they try to stamp it out. Although our politicians could postpone the inevitable, they will not be able to stop it completely. At some point, the number of "illegal" clinics will, because of public demand, reach a proportion beyond the ability of the law to control.

The last part of the lesson from the Soviets is that the turmoil resulted in a horrific amount of damage. Both economic and personal casualties were on a scale we in Canada simply cannot fathom. Even as the economic changes in Russia are now finally beginning to reduce shortages and bring back some choice, millions of ordinary Russians have been left so far behind, to struggle with poverty and disease, that they stand no reasonable chance of catching up. In the same way, a meltdown of Canadian health care would leave a frightening legacy to those caught in the transition—one that could take a generation to repair. The extent of the damage done and the time needed to fix it depends mostly on how far the government will go in trying to maintain the status quo. This is why I do not venture a guess as to when the collapse will actually occur. Our governments cannot stop this process, but they are completely in charge of when it occurs, and how much misery ordinary Canadians must endure in the approach and transition.

Why have we allowed this to happen? We are all, to a large extent, products of our past—and our connection to our health-care system is no exception. It came to us as part of a world-wide humanitarian movement, born from the same fires that drove the largest social experiment in human history. Unfortunately, it came bundled with the economic thinking of that time, and it formed what I call the *Dominant Model* of how health care is delivered. The characteristics of that model are the displacement of "need," as expressed by individuals, with an allotment system, and the ignoring of money and its functions of incentive, reward, and information that it performs in natural markets. I call it the *Dominant Model* because it has successfully displaced all our economic behaviours and assumptions that would normally operate in other areas of endeavour. No one would think of trying to operate even a candy store with those rules. Yet, the *Dominant Model* is so pervasive—and so tied to our humanitarian interests in health care—that it has created its own culture which seems impossible to change.

But there is another way. We could achieve our humanitarian objectives, retain public control, and still provide the health services we need if we made the switch to a more successful economic model. It would take a leap of faith and a series of admittedly unlikely events, but could happen.

Our governments, both federal and provincial, could conceivably take the lead in recognizing the direction in which things are heading, and acknowledge the role they have played in assuring that direction. At least in theory, they could—if they chose to do so together—take the necessary steps to adjust our national objectives, correct the shortages, break up the incentives that maintain our current power structures, and give the public system the stability it needs to survive the next generation. It would take a change in thinking at the very top level of our government. It would require real leadership instead of just following accepted practices. And, finally, it would take political courage—not for the usual cynical reasons, but because politicians are themselves caught in the same paradigm of the *Dominant Model* that controls us all.

Just what changes would need to be made to achieve this reversal are the subject of the rest of the book. It requires a hard look at our assumptions and what it is we really want to achieve. But first, before we can take that journey, we must take a more detailed look at each of the major contributors to the mess we are in. Only after understanding what each player offered can we appreciate what is needed to fix it.

THE PLAYERS

Part Two

THE HOSPITALS

The Complaint

"That's it! I've finally had it with this place. You people are the most incompetent bunch of pompous asses I've ever seen. I'm never bringing anyone in my family back to this hospital again."

Listen to the resounding anger of an unsatisfied customer. In any other industry, these are the most feared words any organization could hear. Losing return business is the first step in the direction of financial collapse, the closure of the organization, and the loss of everyone's jobs. But if you listen closely to this exchange, you will hear no nervous apologies, no hasty demonstrations of gratitude, and no humbling oneself at the feet of the mighty consumer. If you hear anything at all, it will be peals of laughter.

What? Not come back? Lose returning business? Why, that is the most helpful thing anyone could say to this hospital, thank you very much! Instead of a threat, the hospital's executives see the saving of a few precious dollars that could go to satisfying any one of the other urgent needs of the organization. The nursing staff might see less pressure in their work, or perhaps a little grace time to enjoy their jobs. The actual personal encounter might be unpleasant, but the one thing no one in a health-care institution will see is a financial loss to their organization.

The story isn't meant to belittle the professional pride and attention demonstrated by all people in the health-care industry. No one actually enjoys being told they have failed at their work or caused damage to someone else. The point is, everyone has a balance between their professional pride and the amount of pressure they can physically manage at their work. Once that pressure reaches the point where it begins to interfere with the quality and the enjoyment of the tasks people face, any relief from that pressure takes on heightened value.

A good example is cardiopulmonary resuscitation (or CPR). The 1970s saw many advances in medical care, of which CPR was one. No longer did doctors and nurses have to stand idly by watching as their patients died. The process of death became re-named "cardiac arrest," and the technique of resuscitation, now widely known as CPR, was something in which all staff took pride. Stories of miraculous returns to life became legendary and almost commonplace, both within the hospitals and on the street, as paramedics gradually honed their skills to the same standards as doctors and nurses. A successful resuscitation was cause for cheer and made everyone associated with the event feel positive about their job and their role in the health care process.

The situation could hardly be more different today. People still go through the motions, of course, but a successful resuscitation is now a cause for long faces and sometimes tasteless jokes, rather than celebration. On the contrary, aggressive attempts to obtain "do not resuscitate" (or DNR) orders from patients or family members are the activities of the day, and have replaced resuscitation itself as the sustainers of staff morale.

Of course we know more about CPR now, and respect for end-of-life decisions such as DNR is one thing. But a turnaround of priorities on such a scale, within an industry whose central purpose is the saving of life, is disastrous evidence of ill health within the industry itself. Such perceptions and habits, once established, are hard to turn around, and there is no guarantee that the fine distinction between salvageable life and inevitable death is always observed, or indeed recognized.

Why is it that such a reversal of incentives has prevailed within a country that prides itself on its commitment to health care? Why is it that, having successfully removed the profit element and its potentially negative incentives from our health system, we are left with a perverse system that rewards driving needy people away and ending life instead of saving it? To understand the answers to these questions, we must again look at history. Only by examining the smoke trail left by the evolution of government-based health care can we appreciate what went completely wrong, and why it went in the only direction it could under the circumstances.

Global Budgets Come to Visit and Decide to Stay

Prior to the 1960s, hospitals in Canada were of mixed origin and financial background. Some were purely government enterprises, but most were either the beneficiaries of charitable societies—such as the Catholic hospitals—or private. It is wise to remember that even the Catholic hospitals were private, in the sense that they were owned and operated by a private group even though they were non-profit in orientation. In fact, it was difficult (and still is) to run any hospital for a profit in the true capitalistic sense. Sick people are simply not a ready source of cash, and humanitarian concerns, then perhaps even more than now, prevented the unreasonable withholding of care. Even if this were not the case for the senior executives of a hospital, it remained true for the staff. People who go into nursing and medicine are a notoriously humanitarian lot. They tend to make poor entrepreneurs.

It is worthwhile to note that Canadians nowadays tend to confuse private ownership and profit, often assuming they are the same thing. In doing so, we disregard the millions of individuals who are driven by charitable intentions, and as a direct consequence of that disregard we have banished from the Canadian health industry hundreds of organizations that were willing to work tirelessly for us on a non-profit basis. In the U.S., for example—a place we love to hate for what it does to health care—over 85 percent of so-called "private" hospitals are actually non-profit organizations, such as churches, community groups and charitable societies. "Non-profit," of course, does not indicate a desire to operate at a loss, so financial viability still requires fees and accounting systems as well as a choice of mission (also known as "market segmentation"). In reality, these hospitals must aim for a financial surplus to act as a cushion and minimize their risk of bankruptcy. Money collected over and above their actual expenses, however, goes not to any shareholders, but into improvements within the facility. Whether or not this is "desirable" is not the point so much as how little many Canadians seem to understand about non-profit operations within the context of private ownership, and the extent to which they confuse anything that is not owned by government with capitalist-style profits.

Before the 1960s, most Canadian hospitals operated in a similar way, at least from the financial perspective. They did their best to provide reasonable care, charged people or their insurance companies what they could, and tried to stay out of the red while ploughing any surpluses back into the organization. The advent of medicare changed all of that, but not right away. As originally formulated, medicare was a government-based insurance scheme— one that replaced existing health insurance policies with the force of the law, ostensibly to ensure that everyone had health insurance coverage. This was a laudable objective, but if that was the aim, why was the Medicare Act not designed to merely subsidize those who could not afford coverage, and leave untouched the majority of individuals who had perfectly satisfactory health coverage through their existing insurance schemes? In other words, if filling in the cracks in the wall could have satisfied the same objective, then why was it necessary to build an entirely new wall?

The answers underscore the ideological agenda behind the Medicare Act, as well as the economic events it unleashed. The first answer was that it was not only important that everyone have coverage, but that everyone have the same coverage. A mosaic of some people having better coverage than others would not do. So, the Medicare Act was more than an attempt to ensure everyone had adequate treatment—it was just as much a social statement that all people are the same and no human being should be able to feel more privileged than anyone else. The same political statement can be found in other actions from the federal governments of those times, such as the Canada Pension Plan, Old Age Security, and the Family Allowance Plan. All of these by design included every Canadian regardless of need, just so that government could say everyone was being treated as equals even if the money was eventually clawed back in various taxes. All remain more or less in place except the last one, which gave every household a monthly cheque during the 1950s and 1960s based on the number of children in the family, regardless of the income they already had. Eventually the plan was scrapped during the 1980s, when the cost became prohibitive—a targeted allowance based on need was instituted instead.

The values of those times—to appear to treat everyone strictly as equals, regardless of cost—is the legacy inherited by medicare, and is why to this day, attempts to change it to a more secure economic footing provoke such angry reactions and mob-like protests. That is also why economic arguments and examples of current problems are irrelevant. No matter how severe the problems, and no matter how persuasive the arguments, medical care is not being defended so much as a political-social statement is being made. Those making the statement are defending it with a vengeance, and (though they may not know it) with their lives, and with the lives of others.

Some may misconstrue these comments as a tirade against one of the fundamental tenets of social democracy and humanism—namely, the principle of human equality. Nothing could be further from the truth. My comment is not anti-humanist, it merely points out that in Canada, health care is inextricably tied to this concept, to the point where the two become routinely confused in debate. Again, some might feel that nothing could be more natural than a tie between such a fundamentally humanist concept and the provision of health care. Perhaps, but one must remember that health care, although important, is not the only important social mandate. One could argue for example, that adequate food, shelter, basic education, and income are just as important, if not more so. It might be instructive to know that there are societies that have attached all of these principles to the principle of human equality, with disastrous consequences. No matter. For our purposes, it is only necessary to acknowledge that our politicians chose health care as the flagship of their principle of national equality, that this was a conscious political act, and that we will forever confuse rational discussion about ways of improving health care, because it is impossible now to talk about health care without somehow involving the principle of human equality.

The second part of the answer is that medicare changed the incentive structure within the world of health care, from one in which government was a passive agent to one where it could assume direct control and thereby enact its own interests. For those interested in social engineering, it was a glorious day. But the glorious part did not come right away. The initial incentives were not about social change, but about money.

Easy Money

At first, the introduction of medicare caused little noticeable change. Hospitals continued to bill and get paid for what they did. The fact that they didn't have to worry about being paid was a welcome relief to most institutions. The damaging effect on private insurance companies drew tears from almost no one, and the politicians basked in an aura of humanitarian goodness. Costs, however, quickly began to escalate as the readiness of government as a cash source became apparent. It only took a few years to realize that simply taking advantage of a different accounting system could save a lot of money.

It was apparent, to anyone who took the trouble to look, that hospital activities changed little from year to year. In spite of the work involved in tracking and billing each patient and operation that was done, hospital capacity and costs remained much the same except when large infusions were made for capital projects, but that was another story. That rarely happened anyway. Because almost all payment had become a provincial government liability, it made sense to simply repeat the previous year's allotment, plus or minus a small adjustment for inflation or population growth. The Global Budget was thus born. With a stroke of a pen, hospitals no longer needed to do detailed accounting and billing—lowering their costs, and, since the government was the sole payer, passing that saving on to government. Although exact numbers are difficult to find, it is estimated that government stood to save between 10 and 15 percent of their costs with this one policy change. Better yet, since the savings were from a reduction in administration, they came without any negative effect on care to patients.

Once the concept of global budgets caught hold, the idea could not be stopped. The savings were huge and immediate, and made more money available to finance improvements in care. It didn't take long before all Canadian provinces had switched to global budgets for their hospital expenditures.

It seems incredible, now, to think that such a massive saving could come without some cost—if not at that time, then somewhere down the road. Such a thought did not seem to occur to anyone at the time, or if it did, no one was prepared to let on. While Americans continued to be enslaved to their accounting systems, driving their costs of health care up to the highest in the world relative to GDP, Canadians basked in their cleverness and self-righteousness. It was one more body blow in our favour in the ideological battles over the contention that money and health care should not be allowed to mix.

The first sign of trouble came during the early '80s, when some hospitals began making demands for increases in their base rate beyond the traditional inflationary amounts. The argument was that population shifts meant some hospitals experienced more increases in workload than others. Even though adjustments for population changes were at least conceptually part of the funding formula, the census numbers were hopelessly out of date relative to the urgent financial needs of the hospitals. To make matters more complicated, not all patients cost the same to look after, so those hospitals which pioneered new treatments that produced better outcomes—but were perhaps more costly—were left to find other ways to fund their costs. Perhaps worst of all, patients simply refused to play ball by sticking with their local hospital. Instead, they chose hospitals based on referral to specialists, loyalty to their own physician even after they had moved to a different community, on reputation, and sometimes simply based on how they had been treated there the last time (imagine their nerve). In the meantime, pressuring patients to stay with their local hospital would have at least partially solved the problem, but would have been politically risky, to say the least.

It should be remembered that there was considerable wariness on the part of government, the payer, about perceived "empire-building" on the part of some of the hospitals. Government had no assurance of always getting their money's worth from any particular hospital. Changes in demographics and medical practice only made this issue more confusing. From the point of view of government, then, the only way to be assured that they were getting maximum value was to restrict the money while hospitals were forced to keep the amount of care constant, and wait until the cries became loud enough to notice. From that standpoint, most people in government did not consider some increase in financial pressure on the hospitals altogether a bad thing.

The first sign by government that some improvement was needed in the budgeting formula came in the early '80s with the popularity of ZBB, or zero-based budgeting. The term was coined in the U.S. to reflect the philosophy that hospitals (or any other institutions, for that matter) should not expect to simply receive the same money from year to year. Instead they should expect to justify ALL of their budget anew each year. Instead of setting the zero mark at last year's allotment and making adjustments from there, the ZBB concept dictated that the real baseline each year was zero. The theory was that once the first year's budget had been justified—admittedly, a lot of work—then only the changes needed to be tracked thereafter, ensuring that the gains resulting from global budgeting would not be entirely lost.

Although the idea seemed sound, the execution was a disaster. After years of having virtually no budget preparation, hospitals simply did not have the expertise or information needed and were unable to cope with the work of the first budget. Within a few years, governments gave up and the idea of zero-based budgeting was left behind in the dirt. Global budgets, based on the previous years' allotment, were here to stay after all.

The first impetus behind global budgets was the need to save money, and global budgeting certainly did that. No one knows for sure how much was saved, but we can afford to be generous on this one and assume all of it went back into health care. So what went wrong? It seemed like such a win-win situation at the time. Why did global budgeting turn into such a disaster?

The problem with global budgets is that at the same time as we saved money, we gave up information. Now, after twenty-five or so years of global budgets, no one knows any more how much anything costs. We know how much we are spending, of course, but we don't know what we are getting for it. We don't, for example, even know what an appendectomy costs. It is now the 21st century, and we have progressed to the point where we at least have the systems in place to figure out what an appendectomy appears to cost in one particular institution. Some have done just that, but why should we expect any agreement on those costs from one hospital to the next? All of them will come up with different figures, and there will be no way to know who is correct.

Why is this important? Because if we lack information on costs, we also lack the information we need to make sound financial decisions. Why should we pay $10,000 for an appendectomy at one hospital if it only costs $5,000 somewhere else? If the costs are that different, shouldn't one hospital be looking at its practices? If we don't know what it costs us to do things, then we will get no feedback to improve. Maybe we won't even know there *is* a problem.

Twenty-five years or more after global budgets began, the information we need to fix things is hopelessly lost. Reconstructing it will be a major undertaking that is sure to provoke animosities within the industry. But we come back to the main question over and over—even if we can't do anything about it, isn't it important at least to know?

Doing the Budget Waltz

It is the 21st century and we have become more refined about the way we do global budgets now. Instead of approving a fixed percentage over the previous year as we once did, we have a new idea called PBF, or Population-Based Funding. Adjustments to hospital global budgets are now made using a formula that includes information on past patterns of use, population shifts, and even on referral patterns.

Is it a significant improvement? Perhaps it is better than a crude percentage—however, significant problems remain. For example, the formula cannot consider the choices people make about the medical care they get in hospitals outside their district. It also fails to take into account the changes in society. While the formula is adjusted for population age and sex, many provinces do not bother to adjust for socio-economic indicators, even though these are known to affect the amount of health care a population requires. Lastly, the formula—such as it is—is often ignored anyway, since the amount given to each hospital can be overridden by political discretion. In many provinces, hospitals routinely receive no budget information until several months after the year-end.

Hospitals are supposed to manage their budgets, but have no control over demands placed on them by patients, and no feedback on what their costs are, relative to other hospitals. The net effect is that hospitals are actually being punished for providing good care, because they attract patients while their budgets remain rigid. In some provinces, hospitals are actually penalized with lowered budgets if they are deemed to be providing "too much" service, because they are accused of "driving utilization."

The fact is, population-based funding is still just another way to calculate what amounts to a global budget, and under global budgets, hospitals only have two ways to avoid a deficit. One is to curry as much political favour as possible so as to receive favoured treatment. The other is to convince patients to go somewhere else. They do both with vigour.

The Gatekeeper Theory

The 1980s became replete with a variety of management theories on how health care should work. Some of these are reviewed in more detail in another chapter. The major one, and the one we will focus on here, was the gatekeeper theory. Briefly put, it proposed that since both the users and providers of health care were not paying for anything, their appetite could be expected to have no limits. The only way, therefore, to keep the store from being totally raided and depleted, was to install "gatekeepers" invested with the authority to limit the amount of resources actually being used. The obvious similarity to simply rationing health care was countered by the supposition that these gatekeepers were acting not out of political direction, but with a wider knowledge and understanding of what was actually needed by the population. The science behind gatekeeping then was the newly emerging methods of calculating utilization rates, and comparing them with other jurisdictions.

It was a science with broad natural appeal, such that it seemed to need no testing. Typical observations were that gallbladder removal rates in Canada were five times as high as in Great Britain, with the obvious conclusion that we were taking out too many gallbladders here (from *Second Opinion*, by Michael Rachlis). The suggestions that perhaps not enough were being removed in the UK or that other factors may have been involved were given short acknowledgement.

That was because the prevailing assumption was that hospitals were doing too much, driven by the physicians' need to make money and emboldened by the ready source of cash that government represented. Given this inherent suspicion, the tendency was to look for and accept only evidence that supported the theory. Research, therefore, that supported the mainstream hypothesis was supported, while contrary evidence was viewed with what often became career-ending suspicion.

In the meantime, a virtual army of health-care administrators dutifully followed the prevailing philosophy of the time, carving restrictive policies into the fabric of hospital management structures and taking pride in the fact that they were protecting medicare in the process.

The natural defence lines in the gatekeeping process were admission to a hospital bed, access to advanced diagnostic testing, and the process of booking an operating theatre for elective surgery. In the first instance, a simple restriction on the supply of hospital beds was the easiest and most effective way of limiting use. An open run on these beds was prevented by the emergency department, which was honed as a method of identifying legitimate emergencies requiring an in-hospital bed. The emergency physicians and nurses then became conscripted into the army that protected in-hospital beds from unreasonable use. Naturally, the admitting physicians and surgeons became the enemy that could be expected to pressure the resources—partly because of their own financial interests, but equally because of what was seen as their ignorance of the larger picture, revealed only through the science of utilization. To this day, nurses (and sometimes emergency physicians themselves) become upset at what they see as the "back door admission," referring to the pretense of an emergency complication merely to get a patient into a bed that could not be accessed any other way. Many physicians simply accepted their role as perpetual adversaries of hospital administrators, the one representing the interests of the patient and the other defending health-care dollars.

As long as the dynamic balance was stable, the structure was not an intolerable way to way to carry on.

A fine line exists between the science of utilization and the hard limits of finance. This is especially true when decisions that create the financial envelope are arbitrary and political instead of based on evidence. It is a line that was crossed in Canada long ago, even as the faithful army of gatekeepers soldiered on, following their policies and procedures set in better times. Utilization science was never intended as a foundation for barriers to access. It was intended, instead, as a way to anticipate future needs and uncover reasons why marked differences existed from one region to another. Since the use of utilization measurements to limit access to health care in Canada was an abuse of the process, rather than a feature of the method itself, we should not blame utilization science for the way it was used.

Games Hospitals Play

One must understand the frustration of politicians and provincial health management staff in order to appreciate the events that followed. On the one hand, these people had the ultimate power in the form of control of funding. On the other hand, they held virtually no means of control, aside from the big stick of withholding funds—which was politically dangerous. Their frustration was that they had no means of fine-tuning their control over the policies that individual hospitals chose to follow.

Naturally, their concern was about activities they deemed, from their central vantage point, to be wasteful. Those inexperienced in this kind of surveillance might wonder, "What can be considered wasteful about health care? Activities either help patients, or they do not."

Or is it that simple? Heart surgery, for example, may be performed in more than one location. If a central agency is paying for everything, why should it pay for two services that do the same thing but operate across the street from each other? There is an urge to centralize anything that is more expensive, to eliminate the waste of duplication. This is in direct contrast to the urge within each hospital which tries to maintain its own expertise, its own staff, and its own prestige in the community.

The contrast between the view from the top, as it were, and the view from within each hospital underlies a complex clash of models, with several manifestations that have directly affected our health-care system.

The first of these manifestations is "rationalization." The term will be explored in more detail later, when we discuss the fads in health-care policy. Suffice it to say, that it seems "rational" not to allow two hospitals to provide specialized services when one will do the trick. The real clash here is between the supporters of competition and those who support the model of central control and planning. It seems better to plan things so as to minimize waste. But the same theory that wants to deny two hospitals that both do heart surgery would eliminate a Macy's across from a Sears and allow only one large department store to supply everyone's needs. Why do we have two large airlines flying the same inter-island routes within Hawaii? Would it not be less costly to only have one and save the supportive costs?

One can see the head-on clash between two very different economic theories. It seems reasonable that one provider should be better, but every jurisdiction that has tried to do this in non-health related fields has failed. Why do we insist on repeating the experiment in health care?

To be fair, the one-provider concept also finds support within much of the medical community as well, for reasons that are not in any way financial. Studies show that centres performing complex surgery below a minimum frequency cannot achieve the same level of skill demonstrated by those who do it all the time. It is natural also for large hospitals that do heart surgery, for example, to want to keep all the business for themselves. At the same time, if experience is needed to become better, how is a second hospital with the resources to do the same thing ever to get the experience without starting somewhere? How do we separate true excellence from a desire simply to avoid the nuisance of competition?

This is not a controversy that we will solve here, nor do we need to do so. At this point, all that is necessary is to understand that there are two fundamentally conflicting points of view here that are not easily resolved. The take-home at the end of the day is that, ever since the advent of medicare, the relationship between government and hospitals has been founded on a basic mistrust. Governments and their ministries of health mistrust what they see as empire-building agendas on the part of individual hospitals, while the hospitals in turn mistrust what they see as clumsy micromanagement and interference in their strategic decisions.

Each side manages the relationship through an elaborate system of games. The chips in the game are funds allocated by government, and the rules involve the control of information, and politics. Caught somewhere in the middle are the patients, who think their patronage or loyalty to a particular hospital is valued and that hospitals gain something by ensuring their needs are met. How wrong they are.

It would be unrealistic to expect a governing body not to take the steps necessary to stabilize and protect its own point of view. There are two ways in which governments can make sure that their own agendas are respected.

The first is simple micromanagement of the funding supply. Money is allocated to individual hospitals only for processes that meet the approval of the central authorities. Hospitals are thereby stripped of any significant power to determine their own fates, and may even be punished for failing to follow the rules laid down by their superiors.

The second, a more subtle technique, consists of forcing the hospitals to belong to regions defined by the provincial government. Each newly formed region is given a mandate to provide health services within its own geographical area, that mandate being embodied in its Regional Health Authority (RHA). Generally the boards of the RHAs are political appointees and can therefore be trusted to stay within the broad mandate set by the provincial government. The key is that individual hospitals are forced to fight for resources, not from the ministry, but from other hospitals in their own region.

Most provinces have formed Regional Health Authorities, while Ontario has preferred to go the route of individual funding for hospitals and maintaining planning control centrally within its ministry of health. The methods may vary, but the fundamentals of the game remain the same. It is all about money.

Taming the Lion

No matter how you look at it, hospitals are important. They have become the place where the bulk of care is actually provided and they consume the lion's share of the health-care budget. Across Canada, hospital costs consume about a third of the entire health-care budget. This compares to about 20 percent for doctor's fees, and about 10 percent for other institutional care. Clearly, controlling the expanding costs of health care cannot be done without controlling the biggest spenders of them all, the hospitals.

The biggest component of hospital cost, as in almost any business, are the labour costs. In the case of hospitals, this boils down to the nursing and other labour costs associated with caring for a patient in bed. The key to controlling hospital expenses, therefore, is to control the number of beds.

But how many beds does a hospital actually need? The naïve answer would be, "As many beds as there are patients." Unless, of course, you believe hospitals are admitting patients unnecessarily, doing procedures that do not need to be done, and keeping people in hospital longer than absolutely necessary. And this is precisely what the policy-makers controlling health care funding did believe.

In 1970, the average number of hospital beds per 1,000 population was over five. Gradually this number decreased, as funding under medicare exerted its influence. In 1991, when the BC Health Commission made its recommendations, it had reached 3.25 and was still falling. The Commission recommended a target of 2.75 beds per 1,000 population as a reasonable target by the year 1996.

How do we know how many beds are really necessary? The answer is... we don't. What we do know is that the ratio of beds to people fell during the 1980s and early '90s without any apparent ill effect, if one ignored the protests of the health professionals. The difficulty was that some regions had different bed needs from the average. Referral hospitals, for example, always need more beds, because they do some of the more intensive work for other regions. An overall average that was exactly right could hide the fact that there were severe regional disparities, with some having more beds and some less than 'necessary.'

One fact remained clear—as long as the process of bed reductions did not create a resounding hue and cry, they would continue because they were the major way governments could save money. By the end of the 1990s, BC had reached an average of 2.27 beds per 1,000—well below the number recommended by its own Commission nine years earlier. The question was, were patients suffering?

To be fair, much had changed in medicine over the past 15 or so years, and has continued to change. In-hospital stay for an uncomplicated heart attack is now four days instead of ten. Heart bypass surgery patients routinely go home on the fifth day after surgery, instead of after two to three weeks. Many cases that required open-heart surgery a few years ago can now be done with a day-care procedure called angioplasty with equally good results.

Routine maternity cases are now sent home on the second day after giving birth instead of the seventh day, as was the custom in the '70s and early '80s. Gallbladder surgery used to be an open incision with a seven-to-ten day stay, but is now done with a fibre-optic scope through a keyhole incision, usually with a same-day discharge. These are only examples of progress in reducing hospital stay and costs without harming anyone, and even improving the care many patients receive. But it is a slow process of learning, and the reductions cannot go on forever. At some point, the cut reaches bone.

By the late '80s, anecdotal reports of patients unable to access care were becoming frequent enough to arouse attention. Governments were quite willing to tolerate delays in accessing elective care, but were careful to point out that anyone who had a true emergency would be looked after promptly. The anecdotes, however, were increasingly about emergency care, not only elective care. Typically, the response of most of the provincial governments was either silence or the counter-argument that hospitals could always increase the resources they devoted to emergencies if they gave up some of their electives.

And give up their electives is what they began to do. Remember that governments were still holding firmly to the belief that more elective surgery was being done than was necessary, and tightening the funding was the only way they had to force compliance with their point of view. In the meantime, the definition of "elective" was drifting away from varicose-vein operations and other things people had a choice about, toward surgery for intractable pain, cancer, and even heart surgery. The changing nature of the cases seemed to make little difference. Hospitals simply had to do their best to balance the demands of their emergency departments with "elective" patients competing for the same beds.

By the late 1980s, there was ample anecdotal evidence that the constriction in beds had reached critical levels by impacting on the flow of emergency patients. Ambulance services began to develop 'diversion' policies, preparing what to do in case a destination emergency department was full. The plans were repeatedly modified, ignoring the fact that diverting emergencies was never really a workable option. For one thing, not infrequently more than one hospital was 'on diversion' at the same time and alternates were long distances away. For another, ambulance attendants—though well trained for true emergencies—were not diagnosticians, and were forced through caution to over-diagnose, causing an excessive number of patients to be diverted long distances needlessly. And finally, diversion policies did nothing for the majority of people who walked or drove themselves to emergency instead of taking an ambulance.

By the beginning of the 1990s, some communities made an attempt to turn the anecdotes into hard evidence. Hamilton, Ontario was the first to develop a computer that could track all available beds in the city for the purposes of directing ambulances, but also to keep valid statistics for the first time on bed non-availability. A similar but more comprehensive system was developed for Greater Vancouver and was operated by the Greater Vancouver Regional District during 1992 and 1993. There was now clear data to show that multiple hospitals in the same area were often forced to be 'on diversion' at the same time. The same computer reports showed that "no available intensive care unit beds in any of the hospitals" was also an increasing occurrence. One would think such hard evidence could not be ignored, but it came at precisely the time when governments were most intent on decreasing the supply of doctors and beds. It was in 1993 that the federal government slashed medical school enrollments across the country by ten percent. Clearly, the distrust between government and the hospitals had attained a momentum that could not be stopped by mere information.

Do More With Less

The message from government was clear. Everyone knew there was still 'waste' in the system and there was simply no more money. If we wanted to provide better care for our patients, we would simply have to uncover the wasteful practices, and create the innovations that could redirect the money saved into more productive activities. "Do more with less" became the watchword for the day. A National Forum on Health, created in 1995 by Prime Minister Chretien to investigate the concerns about medi-care after more than two years of meetings, came to four conclusions: (a) the health-care system was fundamentally sound; (b) we were spending enough money on health care; (c) the system could be improved and money used more effectively; (d) Canadians wanted to preserve the fundamental principles of medicare.

Thousands of slightly jaded but still dedicated doctors, nurses, and administrators strove to meet the challenge, using quality assurance methods, committees, or anything else at their disposal. Gradually, the "do more with less" movement settled on three issues that seemed to offer big returns—(a) the long-term care problem, (b) the "hospital without walls" concept, and (c) preventative care.

a)   The long-term care problem refers to the number of long-term care (LTC) patients still occupying acute beds in hospitals, thereby making these beds unavailable for the use for which they were intended. All hospitals had some of these, and some more than others. The idea seemed an obvious one. Long-term care beds were less expensive than acute care, because they required less nursing care. By moving these patients, total costs would decrease, and more acute beds would be freed up for emergency and elective cases alike.

Efforts began with motivating those patients who were essentially getting free rent in hospitals to move into more appropriate accommodations where nursing care was still available, but where they would be expected to pay. Next was dealing with the shortage of places to move all these patients in the first place, as the need seemed to dwarf the supply. Since the underlying assumption was still "no new money," building new facilities was not an option until money could be saved from the vacated beds. That little savings materialized from this approach should not surprise anyone, but governments during the mid-1990s still did not accept the non-viability of the 'exchange' plan. Those hospitals which were successful in moving out their long-term care patients found that a harder core remained of patients who, for one reason or another, were extremely difficult to place. The point of diminishing returns had been reached without a noticeable increase in available beds for acute care.

b)   Going by a variety of names, the "hospital without walls," or home care projects also flourished during the late 1990s. Put simply, the intent was to provide as much of the care people needed in their own homes instead of in hospitals, with their rigid routines and schedules. The aim was to save the costs of the nursing routines and structural costs—such as meals, beds, and laundry—that go into running any hospital. Again, the intent was to turn the savings over to use by acute care. The ideal patients were those receiving intravenous (IV) medication, such as antibiotics, and no other active treatment. Once the IV line was established, anyone with minimal training could give the drugs—even the patient's family members.

Again, a sterling idea became less sterling when put into action. First of all, the safety issues spawned a whole set of new nursing procedures and education that seemed to grow more and more complicated as time went on. Second, the extra number of nurses required on the road to administer the program had to be recruited and funded. Many patients who seemed ideal for the program turned out also to need repeat assessments and other support more easily done in the hospital. Those who did manage to succeed in the venture found that, when all the costs were considered, little or no money was actually saved. Perhaps the project was a success in the sense that it was better for patients to stay in their own familiar surroundings, but not enough beds were saved to notice, and nurses on the road proved to be an expensive item.

c)   Preventive care, like motherhood, is something few people want to denounce. Everyone knows what an ounce of prevention will buy, but few people know how to make it pay. Even fewer know how to make it pay within the time frame decreed by government as a fiscal year. The one exception was influenza prevention.

Studies have shown a high incidence of hospital admission and death from influenza and news of emergency ward crowding is not infrequently blamed on the 'flu season'. It is hard to know whether those who make these statements truly do not know, or are deliberately misleading the public. Anyone who takes the trouble to look would see that emergency ward congestion has become a year-round, endemic problem in almost all Canadian hospitals, having little regard for influenza. That is not to say that flu prevention is not worthwhile, just that flu does not account for the shortage of acute beds and vaccination programs have little effect on emergency ward congestion. This past season, the end of 2000, saw the most aggressive flu vaccination campaign ever, but the numbers of visits for flu-related illness were as high as the previous year, and hospital and emergency congestion were also just as bad.

Prevention, when it finally takes its rightful place, will be seen as something we do *in addition* to looking after the acutely sick, not as something that takes its place. Public policy prevention efforts—such as seat-belt legislation, bicycle helmets, and the crusade against drunk driving—have taken their rightful place as invaluable components of our health system. The reduction in specific disease incidence, however, will always be offset by the development of other ailments. Disease, illness and injury follow a random-but-predictable mathematical reality. No one is aided when we consistently underestimate this need—especially when we expect to use it as a way of saving money.

The Gatekeeper Theory Bites the Dust

And so we come to the end of the road for the theory that started it all—the notion that a system of 'gatekeepers' would keep costs down by controlling the rate of utilization. Some people still find it difficult to accept that something that makes this much sense should in the end fail to live up to its expectations. They could have saved themselves the embarrassment, and the rest of us a lot of hardship, if they had learned a little about queue theory, the science that tells us how waiting works.

The trouble with utilization as a concept is that it consists of averages, while real life consists of a constant stream of random events. The difference is illustrated with a simple analogy. Consider a bank in which a teller handles one customer per minute. If customers come in at a rate of exactly 60 per hour, that one teller should be kept busy, but the question is would there be a queue? If customers came in exactly one minute apart, and if each took the teller one minute, then there would be no queue. Each customer would arrive just at the time the teller was free. That of course, does not happen in real life. Customers come in at their own convenience.

The average time between customers may stay the same at one minute, but if customers arrive at random times, queues rapidly develop. To make matters more complicated, the time per customer will also vary, since some customers take less time and some take more. The averages may remain the same, but the variation itself creates a significant queue of people waiting for the same teller.

That simple analogy is one that health-care planners in virtually all of our provinces fail to take into account when they allocate bed quotas. By looking only at averages, they assume that hospitals should be able to handle the load with the beds they have, as long as utilization stays less than 100 percent. In fact, computer models show that 88 percent is the maximum utilization that can be sustained without creating significant congestion, and when there are special units of small size, that percentage will be even less. The planners have been consistently at least 12 percent short of actual bed requirements with their projections when they rely only on averages.

The second weakness of traditional utilization theories is the failure to take into account the very people forced to wait. If the aim of the system is to save money, that only happens when there is no cost to maintaining the queue. In other words, if those made to wait were silent and unseen, the theory would work. In the real world, that is far from the truth. In fact, we know that those who are made to wait create significant costs that are a direct result of the wait itself. They make repeated visits to their doctor, they require costly prescriptions, and many remain non-functional for their families and for their work. In the end, unless they die or get their care in the U.S., they end up costing the system at least the same as they would have under any event. Often the costs are greater, if their disease has been neglected and they have become sicker and take longer to cure. This simple fact alone—recognizing the cost of maintaining those waiting in the queue—should have made the originators of the gatekeeper theory think twice.

The problem has become compounded now many times over. Occasionally, governments relent and throw some more money into the system, then are dumbfounded when waiting lists continue to get longer instead of shorter. The only explanation that comes to their mind is that more money is not helping. With only a little more sophistication, they might understand that if queues result from the difference between those coming in (arriving on the waiting list) and those going out (to surgery), the length of the waits will only start to become shorter when the second exceeds the first. Increasing the numbers going to surgery will not decrease waiting times until that change in relationship occurs. Since they underestimate the size of the problem, they also underestimate the size of the solution, then wonder what went wrong. This is the simple reason why waiting lists are exploding. Because we have not been tracking the demand, we don't know what it is, and we continually underestimate what is needed to catch up.

Over the years, and largely through policies such as these, our hospitals have become probably the most seriously damaged component of our health-care system. Perhaps this is because at no time have hospitals in Canada had any protection against the whims of government. Unlike doctors, who at least had a political presence with their medical associations, hospitals were in a line authority relationship with government. Any protest could result in subtle forms of punishment, such as delayed budgets, or refusals to fund key projects, or requests to produce endless justification of things that should have needed no justification at all. In extreme cases, government could—with the stroke of a pen—suspend a hospital's entire board and management and replace it with people of their own choosing. In the game of chicken with government, hospitals were more like sitting ducks than chickens. The progressive decrease in hospital beds and supplies continued over the protests of doctors, nurses, and patients alike.

Until very recently. In the last two years, the press coverage of hospital shortages has increased dramatically, to the point where governments have now truly begun to take notice. Most now recognize the mistakes of the past and have reversed their one-time stand against expanding the number of hospital beds. The irony is that now, even when they come up with the money, the beds don't materialize. The new king of the health care scene in Canada is the shortage of nurses and other trained professionals needed to staff the beds.

We have a nursing shortage because, for years, we have been laying off nurses as we closed beds to save money. Some have quit nursing altogether or have moved somewhere else. Many continue to work, but are getting older and cannot keep up the same pace much longer. By limiting their pay increases below what less-trained people earn in other industries, the workforce has further shrunk to include only the most dedicated—and now even they are becoming more burned out. At the same time, we failed to understand the looming need (again, because no one was looking at the market) and failed to apply the necessary stimulus to train more nurses. It is a sad combination: lay-offs, undervalued salary scales, and underproduction of new staff. True, the trend is changing, but how could anyone expect there to be no consequence to decades of such profound mismanagement?

> *Mr. F. S. was a 54-year-old man who called an ambulance because of chest pain. Instead of simply taking him to the main hospital, the ambulance called ahead to the emergency department and was told by the triage nurse that the hospital was on diversion. There were no stretchers available at that time and the wait could be hours. She advised that they divert to another hospital. The ambulance took him instead to a closer but smaller hospital with an emergency department and*

a physician, but with no cardiology services. The diagnosis proved difficult because of a number of confusing factors. Within two hours of admission, however, the patient became much more obviously ill, went into cardiac shock and began losing consciousness. The emergency physician correctly diagnosed an acute heart attack but could not use the usual thrombolytic therapy (clot dissolving) because the patient had also been bleeding from the stomach. What was needed was an immediate angioplasty to mechanically re-open the vessels leading to the heart. The facilities needed to do this were at the original destination hospital, not this one. It only took a few minutes for the doctor to phone the cardiologist who agreed to cancel everything else and immediately set up the heart team if the patient could be transferred on a 'stat' basis.

The original ambulance that had brought Mr. F. S. in was still there and agreed to do the transfer right away. They managed to load the patient into the ambulance, but before they could pull away, he deteriorated into complete cardiac arrest. The emergency physician entered the ambulance and went through all the usual resuscitation procedures, but to no avail. The transfer was cancelled, and the heart team sent home. If Mr. F. S. had arrived at the right hospital in the first place, he would have made it into the angioplasty room and would at least have had a chance. Ambulance diversions are a fact of life now in all big Canadian cities. Most of the time, nothing terrible happens. This time, it did.

THE DOCTORS

Of Bedside Manners and Other Things

For many of us, our idea of a "doctor" was formed, during the 1960s television era, around the kindly face of Marcus Welby, a slightly wrinkle-faced, middle-aged male general practitioner played by Robert Young. The doctor was someone who was there when you were born, and was there when you died. He was there when you needed something for your cough, and was there when you needed advice about your love life. He was there when your baby was sick in the night, and was there when you needed perhaps a pat on the back from a trusted old friend. In some ways, the traditional GP was expected to perform the duties of both a scientist and priest combined.

There are still a few doctors who practice in this way. But for the vast majority of people who finished medical school, nothing could be further from their real work.

Medicine has become a highly technical field, dominated by specialists and sub-specialists. Most of the advances in medical care require a multi-disciplinary team of professionals and a high-tech hospital setting. Heart surgery, for example, requires more than just a trained surgeon. It requires a team of anaesthetists, perfusionists, specially trained nurses, a heart-lung bypass machine, surgical intensive care units, and what seems to be an endless array of machines and devices far too numerous to mention. It also requires staff and support services such as bookings, facilities maintenance, and accounting, necessary in any highly tuned organization. A falling down in any one of these people or systems will ensure no heart surgery occurs, just as surely as if the surgeon were missing.

We might prefer something a bit more personal, but maintaining quality requires a high-volume service that is simply unable to treat each of us as an individual. In one sense, we—as consumers of health care—get to choose. It's either modern medicine and what it can do for us, or the old personal touch. It won't be both. The dilemma affects not only the patients, it also affects the providers of the service itself, the physicians.

Heart surgery is only one example, but most modern medical care could be traced into the same high-tech, multi-disciplinary pattern. The expansion of services to include a host of other professionals is sometimes used to devalue the role of the physician. After all, if patient care is now a team affair, that makes the other (non-medical) members of the team just as important as the surgeon, doesn't it? Why do the doctors still get the lion's share of attention and still make most of the money?

The argument is seductive, and certainly I would not argue against valuing all of the team members, who are all important. Vying for who on a team is the most important is a bit like a parent trying to choose which child in a family is the most important. It is a process in which no one gains and everyone loses. The one truth, however, is that only one person decides when an operation is necessary in the first place, and that is the surgeon. On this decision rests the entire cost / risk / benefit of the entire system. If the

decision to operate was in fact a bad one, the cost of the entire procedure, including everyone's salaries, was wasted—not to mention
the risk and inconvenience to the patient. So that decision is naturally left to the highest-trained person in the organization—or is it?

Physicians feel they have lost a lot of influence over the past
three decades. A generation or so ago, physicians enjoyed a level of
prestige they only dream about today. Hospitals, for example,
rolled out the red carpet to attract new physicians. Benefits, like
free parking, free use of lounges, and cafeteria privileges, were
standard fare for anyone on medical staff. On the wards, doctors
also inspired fear and reverence. Nurses were once taught to stand
at attention and relinquish their seats for physicians who entered
the room or the nursing station. Surgeons, especially, were
renowned for having volatile natures, demanding and receiving
whatever their egocentric hearts desired. There was ample opportunity for abuse, of course, as well as dominance, and these stories
are still told and re-told within the nursing community.

Such stories, though, are now the subject for jokes, rather than
reality. For the most part, physicians have acknowledged the
charges of elitism levelled at them in the past, and have accepted a
more passive role within the health-care hierarchy. This was not so
much because they changed, but because they were forced to, since
the multi-disciplinary system in which they now work depends on
the cooperation of the other players. In part, it was also a response
to democratization in the workplace, and the rise in influence of
other unions.

Some non-physicians, however, felt they were part of a social
vendetta against what they saw as the "greediness" of doctors.
Although this may have originated from left-wing political influences in society, it was by no means limited to leftist politics.
Examples persist in the fact that, in many provinces, the gross
incomes of physicians are still published each year. In British

Columbia, this was started in the 1980s by a Social Credit government—a political party that was supposedly a right-wing bulwark. The practice continues, even though all admit the figures are a gross overestimation of pay because they fail to take overhead and hours worked into account. It seems envy is not limited to any one political stripe, but can be useful to just about any group.

Whether because of guilt or because they simply had no alternative, physicians have taken a beating in terms of their influence on health care. Perhaps some of this was necessary and a wider input was a good thing. What is clear is that once the power to make decisions began to swing to others, it became difficult to know where to stop. The bottom line is, we still want a heart surgeon to do our heart surgery, and a neurosurgeon to remove our brain tumour. But we no longer let them make the decisions to operate or not, because those decisions have largely been usurped by politicians, middle level managers, and a whole set of non-medical health sector workers.

The other development is that physicians, as a group, are finally reacting to what they see as a loss of control and credibility in a health-care system run by non-physicians. The increased militancy that results is leading to more confrontations with government and other unions. The 'northern doctors dispute' in BC, for example, while sometimes painted by the more naïve in the press as a play for more income, was really increased militancy from physicians who felt their opinions had been ignored for too long.

The problem is most severe for physicians who are dependent on hospital activity to do their work. Surgeons, for example, require a hospital for their livelihood and to do what they are trained to do. They tend to have most of their fee schedule "procedure-based," which means they generate only a small part of their fees from their office, and the largest part from surgical procedures that require an operating room, nursing staff, and the full complement of in-hospital care. Yet, they are still considered independent practitioners in the sense that they are not employees of the hospital. They pay for their own malpractice insurance, control their own timetable, and are legally independently responsible for what they do.

In order to be allowed to use hospital facilities, surgeons (all physicians, actually) must apply for and receive "hospital privileges." The process represents a partnership between the physician and the hospital where, in theory, each party benefits from the relationship. The physician, for example, pays no fees to the hospital for use of its operating room (O.R.) and other facilities, even though these activities generate costs for the hospital. The hospital, on the other hand, satisfies itself of the credentials of that particular physician, and needs the services of the physician to complete its own mission. Part of that mission is the provision of emergency care for those who become sick or injured in an unplanned way. Most "privileges" are implicit rather than explicitly stated (which is a problem)—however, the understanding has always been that the surgeon will receive operating time and facilities necessary to do his (or her) cases, and in return will participate in an on-call rotation that makes a surgeon available at all times in case of emergency. The arrangement, in spite of its extraordinary reliance on implied understandings, has worked well. Until recently.

As money became tight, hospitals began to restrict access to their operating rooms as one of the only ways they had of controlling their budgets. More recently, daily shortages in nursing staff have made O.R. closures a more commonplace occurrence and a volatile factor in further slashing O.R. availability. For patients, this is an inconvenience and a cruelty, but for surgeons, it is also a cut in their income and an abrogation of the hospital's side of the 'staff privileges' bargain. Naturally, surgeons resent being held to their own obligations to provide 24-hour call when the hospital reneges on its obligation to provide operating time.

Things Ain't What They Used to Be

Physicians have seen a series of other changes in practice since the advent of medicare, some dictated by the economics of medicare itself, and others as a result of technology or of social drifts that would have occurred, anyway.

The economics of running a medical office, for example, have changed forever. Most physicians still are paid on a fee-for-service (FFS) basis. Each office visit has a dollar value, in other words, and physicians' total income is tied to the number of patients they see. There are weaknesses to this mechanism, of course, but in theory it is eminently fair. The more productive doctors—those who work the hardest—are rewarded the most, and doctors who please their patients are rewarded by the fees from return visits. The reason doctors are mostly paid this way is because, historically, they were paid this way before medicare began—which, in turn, is the case because it is the payment model in all business or contractual relationships. If I need the services of a plumber or any other workman, that person gets a fee for providing a service. No one would want to pay for services they did not request, or which were not performed.

The advent of medicare in Saskatchewan in 1971 created a major protest and even a temporary strike by the physicians of that province. Why? Because they feared that the advent of government would overturn their relationship with their patients and would control their fees. The short-lived strike was not repeated anywhere else in Canada, in spite of the rapid spread of medicare to other provinces.

Were the doctors' fears unfounded? Certainly not. The relationship with patients has been dominated by the presence of government, and has undergone a fundamental change. Whether that is a good or bad thing will depend on one's point of view.

The truth is that doctors have actually done very well under medicare. First of all, their fees became guaranteed. No longer did they need to be concerned that some people would be unable to pay, or that they would decide against coming to the doctor because of worry about the cost. Doctor's incomes rose dramatically within medicare, even though the fee schedule itself stayed much the same. The rise was the result of a decrease in bad debts, and an increase in the total number of visits.

Next, doctors were still guaranteed some right to set their own fees, in spite of medicare. Although this has technically remained the case, from a practical standpoint, the fees paid by medicare are set by negotiation. In some provinces, doctors publish two separate fee schedules—one which lists the fees the government has agreed to pay, and another of charges for people without government insurance.

Finally, doctors were assured within the legislation that set up medicare to be able to opt out at will if at any time they became displeased with the arrangement. Again, this remains technically true, but the economics of opting out are regulated by law in a way that provides a strong economic disincentive to do it.

One can understand, with the guarantees above, why physicians were easily persuaded to accept medicare. The guarantees looked sufficient and the bottom line was much improved. Doctors accepted medicare partly because it was a political reality, but mostly because it was good for doctors, too.

Fee-for-Service Under Medicare

Of course, there was a new reality under medicare if one was paid by fee for service. Even though the medical associations set their own fees, increases that were accepted by medicare were hard to come by, and since medicare patients formed 90 percent or more of office income, little else counted. In the meantime, office overheads rose along with inflation and ate into the good doctors' incomes like rats in a bread pantry. There were still some things doctors could do: they could increase their volume of patients, and if they were GPs, they could avoid low-paying activities (such as in-hospital visits by GPs), and refer more patients to specialists. They have been doing all three.

(1) More patients means a longer day, and ultimately less time for each patient. Since overhead costs are mostly fixed, doctors have to put through a minimum number of patients per day before they begin to make any income at all. A typical GP office practice that sees 50 patients per doctor per day, for example, may experience a 50 percent overhead, so that the first 25 patients generate no income for the doctor—they merely pay for rent, hydro and staff. Fifty patients per day in an eight-hour day leaves only ten minutes per patient—even less when lunch, staff coffee breaks, and changeover times are included. At the end of eight hours, there are phone calls to make, prescriptions to call in, and office management issues still to deal with. Small wonder patients complain they don't get enough time with their doctor.

(2) All physicians know which fees pay poorly, and for some reason, in-hospital visits have always been at the bottom of the pack. The practical side of hospital visits means driving through traffic, parking, long hallways, and waits to hear reports from nurses busy with other tasks. To make matters worse, in-hospital patients are often under the care of a specialist physician rather than a GP, so the whole exercise often seems like a waste of time. On the other hand, patients (and nurses) often complain that specialists look after the part they concern themselves with, and leave the rest of the patient in limbo. Orthopaedists look after fractures, but mismanage the

diabetes, or fail to understand the home situation that the elderly face. Without a GP, patients are often left without advocates to deal with many layers of professionals. GPs are caught between a rock and a very hard place. If they see their patients in hospital, they lose money; if they don't, they abandon their patients to the 'system.' Many hold on to their in-hospital work as long as they can, but eventually everyone has a breaking point. Small wonder so many of them gradually drift to office-only practice.

(3) Perhaps the most noticeable drift in medical practice is the increase toward more specialist referrals. From the point of view of a health economist, this is an absolute disaster. Nothing could be more expensive than the process of specialist referral. It is not the specialist's fee that is expensive, but what occurs afterward. Less than 20 percent of health-care costs arise out of doctors' (including specialists') fees. The rest are generated by the work that doctors cause to happen, and the lion's share of this work is created by specialists. They are the ones with the access to the most expensive tests and procedures. They are the ones who do the surgeries, and cause in-hospital stays.

Most specialists, when asked, feel they themselves are trapped within the system. Once a referral is made, the specialist feels compelled to order tests because the patient expects no less. Otherwise, what is the point of visiting the specialist? Often specialists feel that patients who do not receive tests will deem them inferior doctors and simply go somewhere else. Some of them cite medical/legal reasons for ordering tests, since not ordering them becomes inherently risky when everyone else does. Rarely does a patient arrive at a specialist with any written history whatsoever, let alone the truth. If there were such a note, the truth might be "I could look after this patient myself, but it would take me too long and I wouldn't get paid what it costs me in overhead. Would you mind doing it, since you get a consultation fee that is larger than my fee for doing it?

Attempts to limit referrals have backfired, because there is no way to separate the necessary from unnecessary referrals. As long as the incentives are there to refer, no one should be surprised when that is what doctors do.

All of this sums up to be more than simply costly, and more than unfair to patients. It also ends up being highly dissatisfactory for general practitioners. They know that by avoiding in-hospital practice, they risk becoming irrelevant to their patient as well as unknowledgeable about new developments in medicine. Gradually they risk losing most of their precious skills altogether. Most physicians who have stayed out of hospital medicine for a few years begin to feel quite uncomfortable if for some reason they are forced to return to it. It is a sad fate for someone who entered practice for personal satisfaction.

It also forces hospitals into a difficult situation. Most hospitals understand the value of maintaining a general practice presence, even when specialists carry out a lot of the care. As the GP community pulls out, hospitals are left scrambling trying to fill the vacuum. Those that happen to be teaching hospitals may have enough interns or resident staff to fill the void—the rest, however, are stuck. Recently, some hospitals have resorted to hiring their own group of GPs specifically to do the in-hospital work. Physicians who choose to do this work under contract are called 'hospitalists' and they promise to give the hospitals some level of control over their in-patient population and the costs directly related to that care.

It may not be obvious to some people why this would impact costs. For example, it still takes a doctor's discharge order to send someone out of hospital. It is not unusual, however, for a team of specialists each to finish what they are doing with a patient but fail to communicate with each other. Normally it is the job of the GP to act as a coordinator, but when there is no GP—or the GP prefers to stay in the office that day—patients who are ready for discharge end up staying an extra day or more until someone can be found to write a discharge order. That means increased costs, for no one's benefit. A hospitalist who is on-site will be more available to look after this situation, and even to take pro-active measures to ensure patients are discharged as soon as is reasonable. The system promises to improve care and save money, but of course has no source of funding, because the traditional fee schedules are not set up for this kind of practice. Nevertheless, there is increasing pressure on hospitals to do something about this.

Perhaps the greatest source of that pressure is the 'doctor of the day' problem. Many urban hospitals admit, more and more frequently, patients without a family doctor. Partly this is the result of increased personal mobility—people tend to move more often than in the past. Partly it reflects the intensifying difficulty of getting a family doctor in the first place, as the supply of physicians gets less and less. In many urban hospitals, 50 percent or more of patients admitted have no local GP and must have one assigned from the 'doctor of the day' pool. Generally this is some sort of rotating service provided by the GPs on staff.

It should not be hard to understand that if GPs find it difficult to meet their obligations to their own patients in hospital, they are less than keen to do it for someone they have never met before and are not likely to meet again. Increasingly, these patients are being disenfranchised once they are admitted to a hospital. They are assigned a reluctant GP, if they are lucky enough to get one at all.

Most of the time, they are blissfully unaware of the commotion they have caused by being sick enough to get admitted, and thankfully have no idea that they are at the centre of a protracted war.

Medicare and the Health Service "Contract"

When I see a dentist, or a plumber, or a rental agency, or any other business, a *contract* is set up that governs our business relationship. The dentist (or agent, or whatever) agrees to provide a service that meets certain specifications that I have, and in return, I agree to pay a certain amount of money. Whether a formal written contract is drafted or not is quite irrelevant, since verbal or even implied contracts hold just as much weight in law, as long as it can be shown that a mutual understanding existed.

The presence of an insurer does not substantially change the arrangement. Medicare, however, is no longer acting just as an insurance agent but as an active participant in the provider of facilities, which affects the decisions being made. Medicare, therefore, acts to confuse the contractual relationship between physician and patient.

If you ask patients who is responsible for the care they receive, they will probably say it is their doctor. If we ask the doctor, most will want to accept personal and professional responsibility for what they do, but when most of the care depends on a facility such as a hospital, and when those facilities depend on funding from another source, the situation is less clear. I suspect if we were to ask the politicians or the officials within any provincial ministry of health, most would think it is they who are responsible. They are the ones with the overall plan for health care, and by virtue of being the ones who make funding decisions, they become at least conjoined in the responsibility.

Why is this important? Because it clearly defines who is responsible should a problem arise. In the case of the dentist or the plumber, when there is a problem with the quality of the work done, everyone understands that they are the ones who need to fix it. If the tooth still hurts after the dental work, there is clearly more dental work to be done. If the tap leaks after the plumber has left, he must return and complete the job. In the case of health care, who does the fixing if the product fails to meet expectations?

What generally happens is that the doctors blame their lack of resources, the hospitals blame the bureaucrats, the bureaucrats blame the doctors, and nothing gets resolved. The dissatisfied patient remains that way, and the next patient is sure to be just as dissatisfied.

Who should be responsible when something goes wrong? The truth is that either system could work, if only it were made clear at the beginning. Examples exist in the HMO[2] system in the U.S., in which it is clearly the HMO that people contract with, and to which they pay their insurance fees. They don't seem to mind who the physician is that treats them, as long as they work for the HMO, and when something goes wrong, they expect the HMO to fix the problem.

Our problem in Canada is that we never discuss the matter and allow both the physicians and the public to believe whatever they would like to believe. In the end, when something *does* go wrong, we have no mechanism to establish who is responsible. The physician, of course, may be sued, but will not be held liable for a lack of resources. Some people have tried to sue governments for providing inadequate resources, but our courts have not yet provided any clear leadership on what a province's obligation really is. No one in Canada should hold their breath.

---

[2] The term HMO refers to a Health Maintenance Organization. The phenomenon swept much of the health care services industry in the U.S. during the 1970's and 1980's and relies on the notion that it is cheaper to pay an organization to keep people healthy than to make them better once they get sick. HMOs are corporations that sell comprehensive medical services for a monthly fee.

Finding Alternatives to Fee-for-Service

Since medicare itself is sacrosanct in Canada, and since fee-for-service clashes with parts of medicare, it is natural to find our politicians looking instead to change the way doctors are paid. Even if we accept that FFS is natural in the private world, this is not the private world, and there are some good reasons why some other alternatives would be better. The problem is, although FFS does reward work done, it also encourages doctors to see patients unnecessarily. For instance, a doctor could schedule one or more repeat visits for a problem that could have been scheduled in one visit, thereby increasing his billings. In the same vein, there is no incentive in a FFS system to go the extra mile to prevent disease and keep patients healthy. FFS, the opponents argue, is built on a foundation of fragmented care, mostly limited to acute events, and has created an unwieldy system fraught with problems of quality, clinical variation, and open to waste and abuse. The difficulties with FFS are well explored and decried by Michael Rachlis in his book *Second Opinion*.

The usual suggestion to replace FFS is either some form of capitation, or outright salary. Capitation is a system used in many other countries, including Great Britain, in which patients "sign up" with their GP of choice. The doctor receives a fixed amount on a monthly basis, according to the number of people who have chosen him. Since the doctor is paid the same regardless of the amount of care he actually provides, the incentives are strong to do the most with the minimum time. It certainly looks after the visit-padding problem. There are many variations on the same theme, with an indexing of pay to such characteristics as the age or underlying illness of patients, to better compensate for the ones who require more work, and even blending of capitation with some lower level of FFS.

Salaries are another option—a relatively straightforward one, since the labour laws surrounding salary relationships are well delineated. A major motivator for those advocating salaries is the conviction that physicians should be treated no different than other employees. If salaries are good enough for other workers, why not for physicians?

Salaried physicians pose some problems, though. Salaried workers are considered to be in an employer-employee relationship. For example, full responsibility for all aspects of the work done lie with the employer, as does the responsibility for all costs of doing business. If doctors were on salary, then the government would have to own and operate all the offices that are now supported independently by physicians. The start-up costs alone would be formidable. Government would have to accept liability for all mistakes and lawsuits against physicians—again, a daunting proposition. Furthermore, government would have to guarantee holidays, coffee breaks, in short a full benefit package similar to ones enjoyed by other government employees. Perhaps worst of all, employer-employee relationships are difficult to terminate without elaborate legal costs and risks, as most employers understand. Once in, government would have a hard time backing out, should it regret the move. It is one thing to talk about salary, but what amount of money would that salary consist of? Salaries are negotiated, not imposed; otherwise, no work would be done by anyone. And finally, the situation would give government nominal control over what doctors do, but real control would require an elaborate management structure not unlike what is required in the present system, with perhaps no ultimate advantage. Salaried physicians looks like an attractive alternative until one looks carefully at the detail, and then it becomes anything but.

A blended variation on salaried physicians exists in the "Managed Care" model that replaces FFS with a combination of salary and incentives for health promotion. This model has been much more extensively explored in the U.S. than in Canada and forms a continuum with the better-known acronym "HMO," which we will further explore in another chapter. The managed-care model is an alternative that at least attempts to integrate the delivery of health care with its financing.

The truth is that all of these variations in pay mechanisms, from capitation to salaries and even some managed-care models, already exist in various places in Canada as a result of individual deals. Depending on the situation, and the details of the contract, any one of them might be useful. In spite of this, except where individual circumstances warrant something different, a large-scale change away from FFS for office practice is something doctors in Canada have aggressively resisted.

Although there are undoubtedly successful examples of medical care provided under different fee arrangements, those looking for a magic bullet to solve the problems of doctors' fees will not be encouraged by the latest research. It shows that all of the methods have advantages and disadvantages, but none inherently saves any money.

Social Shifting

Besides their political aspirations, doctors are, after all, just people like anyone else. Traditionally, medicine has always carried the burden of a higher-than-normal workload. Stories of interns or residents working days on end without sleep are legendary, and unfortunately often true. Even after graduation, doctors are expected to operate on an emergency in the middle of the night and still put in a full day at the office the next day. Some smaller towns rely on one doctor for 24-hour coverage seven days a week. We expect our doctors to be selfless when help is urgently needed, and for the most part, the profession has met that challenge.

Not for much longer. Doctors in training as residents in hospitals formed a union many years ago, to work for equality with others in the workplace. Gradually over the years, they have won the right to refuse to be on call more than one night in four, and to limit their "non-educational" workload. They are part of the "Me Generation" that values time off, family and personal activities, and sensible workloads. They are less immersed in the work ethic than the previous generation, and less motivated by the lure of more income. Many of them (at least 50 percent in most medical schools) are women, who want a healthier balance between their professional time and their family aspirations.

All this is well enough, but the older generation of doctors decry what they see as a lack of dedication on the part of the younger ones. It has always been an acknowledged fact that most of what physicians learn is learned during residency and is directly related to the number of patients and cases handled. It is a bizarre myth that doctors learn what they need to know in medical school. They learn it on the job, in hospital internships, or residencies. The limits on work time have the effect of decreasing the amount that new physicians learn, simply by lessening their exposure and experience. The "Me Generation" may be fine for others, but it is producing physicians with less experience and knowledge than in the past.

Many younger physicians sense this, and express a lack of satisfaction and a lack of confidence in their work. One way to improve their skills is to take post-graduate training of various kinds. The result has been an explosion of young physicians seeking extra time in emergency wards at their own expense, to compensate for what they sense is an inadequate preparation by their conventional training. The others, those that move into practice with only their basic training, start practice and learn on the job, or simply fake it, safe in the knowledge that they are protected by the crowd of others doing the same thing. Ultimately, they will learn that people are concerned only that their doctors are nice to them, and can't really tell whether they are getting good care or not.

The Law of Unintended Results Wins Again

In 1995, the ten provincial colleges that govern licensing of all medical practitioners in Canada announced an extra year of training would be required for all new practitioners before their being eligible for licensure. The move was recognition of the pace and complexity of current medical knowledge, and an assurance that new doctors would be given extra time to learn what they needed to know. It appeared, on the surface, to be an advance in medical preparation and a further assurance to the public of medical quality. In reality, it has had disastrous consequences, both on the quality of doctors being produced and on their ability to obtain satisfaction with their careers.

None of this was deliberate, of course, and yet the outcome was as predictable as arithmetic, had anyone bothered to look. That it happened at all is a testament to the fact that everyone is looking after only their own part when it comes to medical education, and no one is minding the overall store. The story, as usual, requires some background history in order to understand the turn of events.

Prior to the 1960s, all provinces required candidates to complete a one-year rotating internship after finishing medical school, in order to get a licence to practice as a GP. Specialty training required an additional four years and was regulated by the Royal College of Physicians and Surgeons of Canada (RCPSC), a body designated by an act of Parliament to carry out this function. The problem was, there was nothing comparable for regulating general practitioners. A group of general practitioners sought to rectify this during the 1960s, and after being rebuffed by the RCPSC, used their political connections to produce a separate and parallel piece of legislation and a new professional authority called the College of Family Practitioners of Canada. The name "family practice" was coined as the name for a new degree to be gained after two years of post-graduate training instead of the one mandated by most provincial authorities.

The next step was to convince the provincial colleges to require the new certificate before licensure. One province, Alberta, thought this made sense and was willing to be the first to start the ball rolling. Unfortunately, none of the other provinces saw a good reason to follow suit, and the momentum of the college faltered at this point. Alberta, in the years between 1970 and 1995, was the only province that required a minimum two years post-graduate training to gain a licence for general practice. Medical schools began to incorporate the two-year Family Practice residencies within their offerings, but it remained a non-mandatory option everywhere except Alberta. Repeated attempts to convince the licensing bodies to increase their requirements from one to two years met with no success.

Until 1993. Finally, the credibility of the College of Family Practitioners had passed the critical point, and there seemed to be a consensus to make the change. Or perhaps a generation had gone by, and none of the boards of the provincial licensing bodies included anyone who remembered why the proposal had been rejected in the first place. Either way, the proposal was accepted by all the remaining provincial colleges, no doubt congratulating themselves on their contribution to medical education. Unfortunately, no one did their homework. If they had, they might not have been so quick to make the move.

The change mandated a two-year training for all graduating medical students, starting with the 1993/94 year. That meant there was a need for twice the number of residency positions across Canada. Government funds residency positions and had never agreed to such a doubling of their costs, so the change had to occur within the existing funding envelope. That meant the number of residency positions per year in each hospital would have to be halved—otherwise, half the residents would be left without funded positions. Simply halving all of them would not do, since hospitals depended on a minimum rotation of residents to staff their units, so the decision had to be made to strip some hospitals of their residency programs altogether in order to make sure that the remainder had an adequate number of positions. This, of course, pitted university-affiliated hospitals against community hospitals that had prided themselves on their teaching programs and depended on them for manpower.

So it came to pass that most of the community hospitals lost their internships and were faced with sudden manpower shortages. This was in spite of the fact that community-based internships tended to be more heavily volume-oriented, and were favoured by the students because they provided more clinical experience. Community hospitals had traditionally encouraged their residents to get involved and manage cases, while learning from the experienced practitioners on site. By contrast, students could spend an afternoon in a university clinic, seeing only a handful of not-terribly-sick patients, learning little medicine and even less about time management under pressure. The winners, naturally, were the university training programs that were heavy on academics and light on experience—exactly the opposite of what was needed to produce better practitioners.

As if that were not enough, the change prompted a rapid but predictable response from the specialty colleges. Medical school, after all, has been just as much about providing a talent show for specialties to recruit their residents as a place to train real doctors. The mandatory two years in a family-practice residency would force all of the specialties to do without residents for a whole year, without providing the specific preparation they felt was needed for their own specialties. For example, family practice required time in psychiatry and obstetrics, while a specialty like orthopaedics saw these subjects as a waste of time for someone who was going to be an orthopaedic surgeon. The answer was for each of the specialty societies to prepare a list of what they would require—all to be done in one year, of course. Since each of the specialties had different requirements, students would have to know into what specialty they would be going before they graduated. In practice, in order to leave enough time for preparation, the choices had to be made in the last part of their third year, well before medical students had even *learned* about any of the specialties, never mind tried them out.

One might think that if the students were being forced to make choices about their careers before they had enough information, they would at least be able to change that choice should they become convinced later they had made a mistake. But this was specifically prohibited by all of the specialty societies, since they had to be sure their quotas were filled, otherwise they would be facing manpower shortages, or possibly would have taken someone else.

Think about it. Medical students were losing their opportunities for training in community hospitals, were forced to make a choice of specialty that would govern their lives before they had learned anything about what the specialties were, and then were being forced to live with that decision, regardless of their subsequent interests or skills. They were profoundly unhappy, but had no control over the situation. They felt if they wanted to be doctors, this was what they had to do.

I don't mean to try to arouse sympathy for doctors who are not getting to do what they would have wanted to do. It doesn't bode well for the patient however, to be visiting a physician who hates what he is doing and wishes he were somewhere else. Worse yet, it had always been acknowledged that the best specialists were doctors who had completed a few years of general practice first, then went back to do a residency in the subject in which they had become interested. The excellence came from doing something they were passionate about, but also from the basis of general experience gained from the years as a GP. It meant that the orthopaedist didn't get flustered dealing with a patient who developed pneumonia or had a heart attack. It meant, also, that the same specialist would not feel compelled to refer any little thing that did not fall precisely within his narrow area of knowledge. When the dust settled, the new arrangement that was supposed to be a benefit for medical education had ensured this kind of quality doctor would never exist in Canada.

Did the wise doctors making this decision intend to do something harmful to the profession and to their patients? No, of course not! Each was doing what was necessary under the circumstances to protect their own disciplines, and there was no one there at the table to speak for the doctors to be, nor for that matter, for their patients. Can the fiasco be undone? Probably not without rescinding the two-year training, or doubling the amount of money being spent on family practice training—otherwise, the same problems are created that the specialties were being forced to solve.

Medicine: A Fractured Profession

The picture is far from that of the kindly family doctor with whom we started. The pressures of change, including but not limited to medicare, have changed the medical profession forever. Medicine has always been a loose association between fields as far apart as anaesthesia and psychiatry. Now, the fault lines have spread further, dividing on economic lines between specialists and GPs, office-based and hospital-based physicians, and those with daytime-only walk-in clinic practices rich in lifestyle, from those who maintain traditional on-call schedules. For many, medicine is no longer the noble profession enshrined in the Hippocratic oath, but just another 9-to-5 job—slightly better paying, perhaps, than most, but still just a job.

A diminishing number of physicians still remember the "old days," when people who became ill went to a doctor for help. It was a simple, two-sided relationship, in which the doctor played the part of the scientist, the healer, the holder of the knowledge needed to cure the disease and heal the patient. The reality is different now. Patients may start off by seeing a GP of their choice, but if anything even slightly complicated is required, they will be quickly shunted into a maze of unfamiliar faces and a bewildering array of procedures, all funded and supported by their friendly provincial government.

One might have reason to think that, over the years since medicare has been in place, there has been a progression. In spite of what physicians may prefer to believe, there has been a trend toward the state being the guardian of health care rather than the physician. Increasingly, the contract is between the patient and the government's delegated health-care provider, whether that be a hospital or a regional health authority of some kind, or the provincial ministry itself. Physicians continue to play a part, of course, but as the hired hand rather than the pilot. Without question, they are considered an important component of the system, but a component nonetheless, and not the central protagonist they imagine themselves to be. Gradually, over time, the public has been adjusting their expectations accordingly. Increasingly now, they trust a hospital's emergency department, relying on the reputation of the hospital but knowing nothing of the particular doctor who will take charge of their care on the next visit. They rely on the communication systems of the hospital to have their records available, keep their medications and tests straight, and to provide the consultants who will ply their technical skills on their frail bodies. Similarly, they trust a walk-in clinic for what they consider less serious ailments, even though they have no idea what the clinic's quality assurance mechanisms are, or how they select their staff. Even when they choose to visit their own family doctor (if they still have one), they have come to expect someone else in the call group will be looking after them that day while their own doctor has a day off.

If there is a desire to continue the traditional one-on-one relationship between a patient and the doctor, there has been little fuel for the flame from either the government or the doctor's side. Once doctors accepted medicare, the control of both fees and resources was a foregone conclusion, and the rest was just a matter of time. Many physicians feel little remorse and even less reverence for the old ways, and most may never remember a time when it was otherwise. It is not clear that very many physicians have even thought about the consequences. The final chapter in the movement away from professional responsibility by the physicians themselves has probably taken place, and lives under the pseudonym of "on-call fees."

Within the last year or so, physicians have pushed their negotiating advantage toward a resolution of the "on-call problem." By this, they mean their increasing reluctance to carry pagers that interrupt their evenings and weekends with emergency calls. Not that there is any argument about the need for physicians to be available on-call. The argument is over whose responsibility it is to pay for the service.

As far as recent memory takes us, doctors have always been on call for their own patients, except at those rare times when they took vacations. Call for emergency situations for other patients is a relatively new expectation that arose out of the development of emergency departments and the increasing mobility of a public that has less and less need for their own physician except at times of unforeseen crisis. Even so, being on-call had value for young physicians who were intent on building a reputation for themselves, were interested in the experience, and could use the extra money. Typically, a physician who signed on for privileges at a hospital agreed to take part in a call rota for his or her specialty, in return for access to hospital resources for treating patients. The hospital received the services of a physician whose credentials were acceptable, and the physician received equipment, nursing staff and beds—and most important for those who relied on surgical fees—access to an operating room.

The system worked reasonably well even after the advent of medicare, but began to break down as conditions in medicare and in Canadian hospitals deteriorated. A shortage of specialist physicians meant that call groups became smaller and their members older. It also meant that larger geographical areas needed to be covered by a smaller number of individuals. Doctors are by nature hard workers, and at first they simply put their shoulders to the wheel and worked longer hours. As the situation continued to get worse, however, they began to reach the limit of their tolerance. At least under the fee-for-service system, they were being paid for the extra work they were doing, but age has a way of catching up with everyone, and the situation was already destined for trouble when things became suddenly worse.

The nursing shortage was something that everyone in the industry saw coming years in advance, but nothing was done in spite of the many warnings. It wasn't only the doctors who were aging and having to compensate for a decrease in numbers. The nursing shortage, when it fell, took its first toll in the hospitals, resulting in inability to staff wards and operating rooms, and therefore in previously unheard-of numbers of surgical cancellations. Emergency admissions could not be cancelled, but booked cases could, and it was these that took the hit on the chin. Booked cases are the backbone of a surgeon's income, and some hospitals saw decreases of 20 percent or more in the number of booked cases coming to surgery. Surgeons who had provided on-call services all their lives suddenly started questioning why they were still carrying a pager for midnight emergencies when their elective cases had been cancelled on short notice without any compensation for lost income. Increasingly, they have refused their on-call obligations, or to be more exact, have refused to extend their on-call to compensate as manpower levels continued to fall. Since there are no alternatives in times of physician shortage, the only alternative became to institute fees simply for being on-call.

Across the country, the latest and most contentious issue that physicians face in their negotiations, as they see it, is the issue of separate payment simply for being on call. Since these fees are in addition to fees for actually seeing patients, they represent a significant additional cost to the system that will not help one additional patient and will be impossible ever to dismantle. The focus by most governments is similar to what happens at the scene of a brush fire. And yet, the on-call fee issue is not a new one, but a direct consequence of the longstanding erosion in the doctors' ability to obtain operating room time for their patients, and an attempt to recapture their lost income. I have yet to meet a surgeon who would not gladly trade an on-call fee for simple, guaranteed access to routine hospital services.

It will never be dealt with that way by government for one simple reason. As expensive as it is to accept on-call fees for every surgical specialty, it is still much cheaper than the cost of fixing the real problem of access to facilities. So, in the end, the economics drive the direction of change and create a significant departure from previous practice. In a sense, the on-call fees constitute an end point on the process of gradual migration of physicians. They have gone from prime healer to hired gun.

So, even while the champagne corks pop as doctors celebrate their newly negotiated on-call fees, there is an uneasy quality to the event, at least in the minds of some of the older physicians. The reason doctors have done on-call for free all these years is that it was an inevitable expression of their professional freedom, and their choice to meet the obligations that go with that professional freedom. Plumbers and dentists both provide on-call services (although the urgency of their obligations are clearly not the same as for a surgeon) and neither expects someone else to pay them for it. They expect to be paid in the normal course of doing their jobs.

The advent of a fee paid by government changes all that. It is an indication that the physicians themselves now accept that it is not their own responsibility but government's to ensure there is a surgeon available. The last vestiges of ownership of health care have been surrendered, and the doctors have done it voluntarily.

Small wonder that physicians are demoralized as a group. They have watched their external influence atrophy, their public image suffer from accusations of commercial greed, their education system falter, and their selfless dedication to their patients go unrewarded. Many leave, and only a fraction are replaced. And yet, when we have appendicitis, or a broken ankle, or a malignant growth, we still expect to get a doctor. No real alternatives exist. Will they still be there for us when we need them?

For now, the new fees represent a victory of sorts for the doctors. But amid the celebrations, the noises of the laughter and the clinking glasses, those who listen carefully will hear a different, softer sound. It is the sound of a large door closing behind them. The doctors have given up an important part of their profession, and there will be no going back.

THE NURSES

I f doctors have their Marcus Welby, then nurses have their Florence Nightingale to contend with. From that self-denying, caring, white motherly image, the nursing profession has moved a long way.

For a start, little or no basic nursing training is done in hospitals any longer. The traditional schools of nursing associated with hospitals, each bearing the reputation of its hospital, are things of the past. Nursing is also no longer a women's profession. It has actively sought and competed for male entrants, who have shown that caring is not a characteristic restricted only to the female gender.

Schools in universities and other post-secondary institutions have assumed the role of supplier of basic nursing education. Nurses now enter the workforce with a bachelor's degree in addition to the classic R.N. (registered nurse). Has the health-care industry profited from the change? The answer is a mixed one. Again, the explanation hinges on an understanding of the history. How we got here has a lot to do with where we actually are.

Nursing During the 1960s

Again, the major changes in nursing—as with the rest of the health-care industry—can be understood by looking back within a 30-to-40-year window. The typical nurse in the mid-1960s was a young woman of middle-class background, with a high school education and a desire for a career with significance to humanity. That is to say, women with aspirations to do law or medicine were generally excluded (or to be more exact, excluded themselves), as were those less ambitious women who were satisfied with, for example, working as waitresses. The distinction is important, because these were, in general, talented and ambitious young women, living in a pre-feminist society, who did not see themselves taking on a major academic commitment, but were intent nonetheless on having meaningful professional lives.

The way to become a nurse at that time was to apply to one of the hospital-based training programs, the choice of program being dictated by geography, or to some extent, by the reputation of the school. Nursing students generally lived together in a residence whether they had other choices for accommodation or not, since nursing schools were run on a philosophy somewhere between that of a paramilitary organization and a convent. Indeed, since many hospitals were run by Catholic orders, the resemblance to a convent was far from accidental.

The school looked after all the needs of the students, including food, uniforms, and basic education, and often provided the main social context for a young girl's life. Discipline was generally a prominent part of the education, and although classroom teaching was provided, the bulk of the teaching was oriented toward the practical side of nursing duties. Most of the institutions provided a three-year program, after which the graduate nurse became "registered" as a nurse, received her R.N. diploma, and took her place in the workforce, usually in the hospital where she had been trained.

I say she, since the classes were almost exclusively women. Things were simple in those days—men went into medicine, and women went into nursing.

University courses in nursing also existed in those times, of course, and provided an alternate route into the nursing profession. By the late 1970s, some universities accepted a two-year R.N. course as a basis for entry, and gave a bachelor's degree to those completing an extra year of training in the university setting. For the most part, however, university degrees were not seen as an advantage, except for those hoping to go into nursing administration or teaching. Those best prepared to work as a typical nurse were the ones who completed hospital-based training programs.

Transitions

Why did things have to change? A lot of forces came into play to push hospital-based nursing off the map. For one thing, many graduate nurses were highly competent people looking for something more challenging to do than blindly following doctors' orders. For another thing, there was a growing need within hospitals, as technology improved, for people with special training as well as for people with the managerial skills and experience necessary to operate hospitals efficiently. For doctors, who were relatively more highly paid, this direction would have meant a drop in income, but for nurses, it represented an opportunity for advancement at the same time as it provided new challenges for inquisitive minds.

As nursing became more technical and more complex, the traditional doctor-nurse relationship became harder to take. Nurses were on the low end of the totem pole—not only in terms of pay, but also bearing the brunt of the sexist side of the relationship. Nurses were not stupid, and those who took on leadership roles within the profession felt a mission to prove it and to better the professional lives of nurses everywhere.

One of the ways to improve status was to improve basic education standards, and that meant stronger emphasis on the university connection. By this time, education was an activity requiring funding, and the universities clearly were in the driver's seat in terms of attracting government money, relative to hospitals that were still dominated by Catholic orders. The two-tiered education process eventually began to swing in favour of those nurses with university preparation, and the death-knell sounded for hospital-based programs. It remained only for the training schools to recognize they had an uphill battle to secure the funds necessary to survive, and they finally closed their doors forever. With their closing, an era in nursing came to an end. The stage was set for some difficult times ahead.

Just as some people are affected throughout their lives by their short stature during adolescence, much of the history of the nursing profession has been dominated by their inferiority complex relative to medicine. This, of course, had nothing to do with the value of their work. Even in the 1960s, hospitals could not have run without nurses, and that is an even more compelling truth today. The sensitivity of nurses results as much from history as anything else, but is exacerbated by the inferior pay nurses receive (the comparison is to physicians), the relatively lower responsibility, shorter education (specialist physicians receive ten or twelve years of post-graduate education), and less recognition by the public. On top of this, the gender issue is still active—doctors, until very recently, still held the upper hand in the hospital hierarchy.

Perhaps those in nursing who still hold an inferiority complex would feel better to know that nurses are the ones who control the budgets, control the critical staffing, operate most of the high-tech equipment, and dominate the hospital committees which govern how the hospitals run. One might say that, in spite of their "lower" position in the hierarchy, they hold the keys to the family car.

Without the cooperation of nursing, doctors would be helpless, and the health-care system would grind to a complete halt.

Are nurses finally reaping the benefits of their just crusade? The answer depends on what nurses—both as individuals and as a politically organized group—decide they want. In some ways, things have certainly improved, but in other ways, nurses may have painted themselves into a even tighter corner.

The Make-Work Cycle

As nursing developed its own power and credibility, those controlling the nursing organizations should have basked in the independence the profession managed to achieve. Far from being the "doctor's handmaiden," nurses now charted their own territory, drafting the profession's regulations and deciding what areas it wanted to claim for itself. Always with an eye toward what the physicians were doing, nursing guarded jealously the right to stake out its own claim. The nursing profession's need to define itself as a credible and autonomous group, distinct from medicine, was an urgent one.

One example of this self-definition was the emergence of the "nursing history," developed originally as a nursing tool. Briefly, nurses do patient assessments with a view to identifying the needs they should address. In the nursing language, the nursing history is an assessment of health background, family and support structures, and dependency on medical intervention. For example, a nursing history might aim to identify whether a particular patient is coping well with their ongoing encounters with the hospital and medical system. If not, certain supportive nursing interventions might be offered. This is in itself a worthwhile objective, and one not well handled by physicians.

Why do physicians have a problem with it? Because the nursing history repeats a large part of the same information as the doctor gets in the medical history. Perhaps in their drive for thoroughness or their need to establish credibility, the nursing history has grown in the last two decades to include a large amount of material not obviously relevant to their job. Just as the nursing history has inflated, so has the nursing examination. Unlike the medical examination, nursing does not try to do a focussed examination on the affected systems, but instead does a screening examination covering all systems and parts of the body.

Why does this matter? After all, nurses do have considerable experience and their observations can certainly be quite helpful to physicians. If nothing else, they act as a safety check to ensure the doctor doesn't omit something. Perhaps it does not matter, but it addresses the question many people ask when they visit an emergency ward, which is why they have to go through their story two or three times. By the time the doctor arrives, some patients are understandably irate about having to repeat their story so often, especially when many of them cannot tell the different members of the team apart. If the information were passed on within the team, this might not happen, but nurses don't take the history to pass it on as much as to record it on the chart for posterity (or the doctor). If history-taking were more of a factual exercise and less of an art, it might be fine to simply accept the history taken by the nurse and not repeat it. Unfortunately, history-taking *is* very much an art, and interpreting a history taken by someone else is simply not possible.

So, we are sentenced to having everything asked twice. Is that such a terrible problem? If we had enough nurses to do the necessary nursing duties, it would be a minor inconvenience only, perhaps well worth it for the extra safety a second history provides. But nursing shortages are hampering hospital activities everywhere, closing beds and closing operating rooms. Isn't there anything within the scope of what nurses have decided to do that can be relegated to a lower importance?

Nurses and Nursing Aides

One of the main complaints nurses voice today is the number of non-professional tasks they are asked to perform. There are a lot of practical things that have to be done to keep a hospital functioning. Besides the clinical care itself that doctors and nurses carry out, patients need to be fed, beds need to be made, and meal trays need to be carried back and forth. When that is done, there are fax machines to operate, phones to be answered, lab specimens to be taken and reports to be filed. Most of this work falls into the laps of nurses, who happen to be on site and more than amply trained to do these tasks.

Or are they over-trained for these jobs? Why do we have a highly trained nurse carrying hospital garbage and answering telephones? Would it not make more sense to hire someone with lower training at a lower pay rate to do these tasks?

Yes, it certainly would, but before rushing to answer the question it would be useful to know that, not so long ago, the wisdom of the day was to do exactly the opposite. The voice carrying that message was none other than the nursing associations themselves. At the time, hospitals used a mix of nurses with nurses' aides and practical nurses (sometimes called LPNs), not to mention volunteers. The aides did a host of indirect patient duties such as bed baths, meal trays, and making beds, and were a source of general support for nursing staff. What they were not allowed to do was give out medications, or give injections. Only a registered nurse could do that.

"Why hire someone who can only do some of the tasks," the argument went, "when you can hire one person who can do *ALL* the tasks?" The argument was that a real nurse could be more flexible than an aide, and therefore, it was more efficient to hire one nurse than one nurse and one aide.

Why have the nurses suddenly changed their tune? It might help to know that nursing aides and LPNs belong to a different union—one that also represents non-clinical workers, such as orderlies, plumbers, electricians, and floor cleaners. Having less to do with that union seemed an attractive option to many hospitals. The cost argument was valid, because there were lots of nurses waiting to be hired and they were relatively eager to do anything. The end result was more jobs for nurses, who were considered more favourably oriented to patient care issues, rather than strict workplace bargaining. More jobs for nurses was what it was all about, and both the hospitals and nurses were the winners. The winners of the first round, that is, but not the match.

But times change, and we have a shortage of nurses now, so it is the nursing associations themselves that are promoting the move back to hiring more nursing aides. The same nurses who were once considered more flexible employees are digging in their heels, and frankly, getting tired out. How did we get ourselves into this mess, anyway?

Nursing Shortages and Other Market Stories

Most experts agree that the current shortage of nurses is probably the greatest immediate threat to health care in Canada. If the term "shortage of nurses" is a surrogate for "shortage of all types of health-care personnel," the statement would be closer to the mark. But I would agree that of all the personnel or resources upon which we currently rely, nurses win the pot hands down. Even more than a shortage of doctors, the lack of nurses to staff hospitals is grinding our system to a lurching halt.

To be somewhat more precise, the real threat to our health-care services is not the shortage itself, but our failure to identify and fix the root causes of that shortage—which remain in place, doing more damage even as we think about it. It is much easier to leave things as they are, since changes cost money and lead to uncertain results. Why should we mess around with something that has done us well for many years? Or has it?

We are told it is an international shortage, not a local problem, as if that were proof that it could not be of our making. It would be much easier to believe this is a cyclical phenomenon or a piece of bad luck that we must simply endure until it blows over. It would be easier because it would mean we wouldn't have to change anything. But the shortage of nurses (I will refer to nurses as typical of all the shortages we face in health care) is not an external force, like a hurricane, that has come through nature to plague us. It is man-made, and has been quietly growing for years, feeding on the very policies we have enshrined in the core of our systems. The reason it is international is because the same instincts have driven all of us—even in different countries—to follow the same ill-advised policies, largely for the same reasons. The problem may be simple, but fixing it will be difficult, indeed, because it will upset a large number of apple carts.

The forces which have created our nursing shortage in Canada are the same forces that create any shortage. These are government policies that disregarded market dynamics, creating a mismatch between the familiar triangle of supply, demand, and cost. If we look at each of these in turn, both the cause and what needs to be done about it become suddenly all too clear.

First, the demand for nurses. As our populations age and our health-care burden increases, it should take no mental giant to understand that the same forces described in chapter one have been at work increasing the number of nurses we need. This should be straightforward. Second, by eliminating hospital-based nursing schools, we have encumbered the process of training nurses to the point where it is harder to get in, nurses are more costly to train, and all of it takes longer than in the past. All of this has been done—and will be defended, no doubt—in the name of quality and enhancing the prestige and value of the nursing profession.

Valuable virtues, but to what purpose if it means we don't have enough nurses to go around? It is easy to quote quality as an objective when the costs are all borne by another party. In this case, the impetus for burdening nursing education came from the nursing associations and post-secondary institutions themselves, while the bill for the entire process, including the cost of fixing the result, was borne by the unsuspecting taxpayer. It was as if someone took it upon themselves to enlarge their house while sending the bill to the neighbours. Even if well-meaning, and even if ultimately of worthwhile benefit, the process was unrestrained and lacked the usual checks and balances that should accompany public spending.

Even if the wave to higher education increased the cost and decreased the numbers of nurses being produced, we should be thankful for the improved quality. This is the argument we will no doubt hear to justify the process. Perhaps, but there is no proof that the resulting increase in "quality" of nurses at the basic level has translated into any real advantage for patients. On the contrary, hospitals increasingly report that new graduate nurses are unfit for the day-to-day routine of hospital care unless they are given a period of apprenticeship. They have been led by their university training to expect something different, and often are disappointed with the realities of the career they have chosen.

What about the increased specialization and skills required of nurses in the new high-tech age? Surely, a university education prepares nurses better for working in the complex environment of modern health care? Unfortunately, high tech is not the orientation of basic nursing education; much of it parallels the medical model of physiology and psychology. Anyway, education for the high-tech environment of modern medicine is best taught as added modules for those nurses pursuing advancement of their career. Not only is the knowledge retained better when done as a post-graduate exercise, the high-tech field itself is changing so rapidly that any training becomes irrelevant within a few years. If the added complexity of basic nurses' training has benefited patients, it is for the nursing associations to prove. Until they do, it is hard to suppress the suspicion that the only ones who have benefited from the change have been the nursing power structures themselves.

Which brings up an important distinction. The typical nurse is a hard-working and dedicated person who wants a stimulating job with some financial security, some recognition, and the satisfaction of helping other human beings at the same time. The political and academic structures of nursing leave many nurses feeling as alienated as if they were a different profession altogether. This alienation has, in the long run, limited them at the same time as it created opportunities for those within the profession with other agendas.

Whether this internal situation within the nursing profession will ever change or not is anyone's guess. The tides, however, are surging, and the waves are fed directly by the forces that govern how nurses are paid.

Let's Make a Deal: Play or Pay?

Just think about it—the way we decide how much to pay nurses (and almost everyone else) is to put a union team on one side of the table, a government team on the other, and let *them* argue about it. The result is an excellent measure of the relative political clout and bargaining abilities of the two sides. The trouble is, it has nothing whatsoever to do with supply and demand. Some may argue that market realities do influence the bargaining process, but the effect is indirect. The resulting deviation from actual market conditions is small at first, but becomes compounded with each bargaining cycle. Since pay raises are always referenced to the previous agreement, the ability of the process to stay synchronized with volatile changes in market conditions is almost zero. Much of the shortage problem today that we face in health care, therefore, is a direct result of our hallowed collective bargaining system.

Remember that the word "market" has become a dirty word to a large number of Canadians. Even those Canadians who support free market principles in other fields consider health "too important" to leave to the uncertainties of market forces. They forget that the short-term uncertainties of real markets are better than the pent-up tidal wave that results when a suppressed market is eventually released. Also, they forget, in this case that the evil "market" consists of our sick, on the one hand, and the very nurses we are training and depending on to run our hospitals on the other. This is a market we can ill afford to ignore.

Not only do our original collective agreements remain isolated from market forces, but they remain fixed for several years, in spite of any changes in availability or demographics. Everyone knows when we suffer an oil shortage that we all pay more at the pumps, like it or not. But when we have a nursing shortage, the price we pay remains the same and the message to staff is "go somewhere else if you think you can be paid more." Not everyone leaves, but the dynamic balance between those leaving and new ones coming can be easily shifted against us by even small changes in the rate of compensation. When we pay our staff less than they can make somewhere else, some of them leave. When enough of them leave, some of us die. Why is that so hard to understand?

But if we want to blame the unions for the rigidity of pay, we should look again. In many provinces (BC is an example), the collective agreements do *not* prevent the employer from paying more than the base rate. It is the hospital associations that have agreed among themselves that none of them would increase the pay rates. For obvious reasons, because if even one did, then all would have to raise their pay within a very short time to match, unless they

wanted to be left with no staff. Their desire to forge such an agreement on limiting salaries is understandable, but the irony is that,
in any other industry, price-fixing of this sort—at least in North
America—would be considered illegal. In health care, we not only
turn a blind eye, we let our own institutions do it and justify it as
a necessary measure. If price fixing is a bad thing in private business, why is it suddenly considered a good thing in the public
domain? What the hospitals do not apparently realize is that, by
trying to stabilize their staff costs in this way, they are actually con-
tributing to the shortage of nurses. The artificially low pay scales
simply force nurses to consider moving elsewhere, or least discourage them from working full time. Again, not all nurses are
affected by this, but it doesn't take many people to shift the
dynamic balance into one that causes increasing difficulty.

Also, I don't mean to imply any greed on the part of nurses in
their attraction to higher rates of pay. For what they are asked to do,
nurses are one of the most underpaid workers in the economy. Provincial governments are fond of comparing dollar rates and claiming
theirs is reasonable compared to the others. None of it matters, of
course, because if they can't get nurses, the market is telling them that
their rates are not high enough for their local circumstances.

How will it all end? We can only guess by observing what happens in other situations of progressive shortage. It is surprisingly predictable, because people always act eventually to protect their own
interests. Attracting new people into the profession is the best alternative, but it has significant up-front costs. Unless the shortage-cre-
ation process is reversed (highly unlikely in the current political climate), the shortage of nurses will become worse and eventually reach
the point where one of the hospitals breaks its agreement and starts
to pay its nurses above the negotiated rate. Some hospitals are already
using other non-financial lures, such as free specialty training and
signing bonuses, to maintain their staff quotas.

The other reason some hospitals will break ranks is the realization that keeping their rates low has not been saving them any money. All hospitals have dramatically increased their overtime costs because there is no other way to get nurses to come to work. So, all are spending more money to provide fewer services. They are all, incidentally, also teaching their nurses that they shouldn't come to work for straight pay when they can wait until overtime rates are offered. The irony is that the hospital that eventually breaks ranks and raises nurses' pay unilaterally runs a reasonable chance of *lowering* its overall costs, simply by reducing the rates of overtime it must pay. One thing is for sure—when that one hospital makes the break, the game will be up with the others. They will have no option but to match rates, and will be hard pressed to avoid an uncontrolled leapfrogging of pay scales.

Good for the nurses. Bad for the planners, because they won't have any assurance of recovering their costs from government or anywhere else. In fact, such leapfrogging is normal—and in the short run, even desirable—as the only way to settle the proper pay levels relative to the supply of nurses. The difficulty is not that it is happening, but the speed at which it will be forced to happen. Had the proper market-observant forces been allowed to work earlier, that adjustment would have been slower and much less painful. Pain, however, will be unavoidable. It was unavoidable in the communist economies of Eastern Europe when they were finally forced to adjust to the real world. It will be equally unavoidable here.

Could this scenario of uncontrolled collapse of our prized health care be prevented? The answer is, yes—provided something is done soon to change the way we do business in this industry. In a free market, some companies would figure it out, survive, and prosper, while others would not, and go under. In our government-dominated, single-provider health-care market, that cannot happen. There is only one boat and we are all on it—a boat with government as captain and nobody else allowed on the bridge. Far from doing anything about this, so far our governments seem not even to recognize their role in the impending disaster.

The Nurse Practitioners Step Out

If nurses taking histories and examining patients makes some doctors nervous, the thought of nurses actually diagnosing and treating without a doctor's approval makes them completely apoplectic. In some ways, the concept of nurses acting on their own is hardly new, and has long been the practice in many remote communities. But the turf battle with physicians that would result should be no surprise to anyone.

The right to diagnose and treat is restricted to medical practitioners in all provinces by some variation of a Medical Practices Act. In actual fact, that age-old right has been copied many times over, with parallel rights being given to chiropractors and many other practitioners of so-called "alternative medicine." Although traditionally, doctors have never felt comfortable with these alternative therapists, they do not incite the same anger among doctors as talk about nurses providing alternatives to medical doctors. Perhaps because nurses are traditionally supposed to be subservient to doctors—in extent of training, but also in the unstated pecking order—one can expect doctors to feel a greater threat. One must remember that doctors still write "orders" and nurses carry them out.

That, of course, is not what the doctors say. They say care by such practitioners would be inferior to that provided by a doctor. Again, they pretend to protect the public, while in fact protecting themselves.

Would care by a nurse practitioner *really* be inferior to that provided by a doctor? The evidence, such as it is, is mixed. What we can say is that most attempts to create nurse-practitioner jobs have ended in failure. The reasons are hard to pin down, and vary from location to location.

In the first instance, there is no clear definition of the term "nurse practitioner." The expression clearly denotes a higher level of function than traditional nursing, which is designed merely as an instrument to carry out a physician's intentions. Nurse practitioners "practice" a profession, much in the way doctors practice theirs. So, what is the difference? To some, there is no difference at all. A nurse practitioner should be an independent nurse who examines patients, gives medical advice, prescribes medications, and makes referrals to consultant physicians, just as most physicians do.

To be fair, almost all proponents of nurse practitioner programs would limit the prescriptions to a narrow circle of relatively safe drugs, such as antibiotics, and would be prepared to refer to a general practitioner rather than necessarily to a specialist. All would envision a different training course, expanded from what nurses currently complete, and all would, at some point, accept medical direction to their program.

So what is the point to having a nurse practitioner? In part, it is a way for nurses as a profession to assert their independence from physicians and to promote what they feel they have to offer. It should be no surprise that nurses—especially those who are experienced in high-acuity situations such as an ER or an ICU—see many physicians who display less knowledge and skill than they do. After years and years of learning in the workplace setting, these nurses feel they have something valuable to offer, and are prepared to offer it to society for much less money than they see physicians receive.

But would they do as good a job? Without question, there is a large variation in the quality of medical care provided by physicians, just as there is a large variation of abilities among nurses. If the question is whether there are some nurses who would do a better job than some physicians currently do, the answer must be an unequivocal YES. The question of whether a cohort of nurses graduating from a practitioner's course could do a better job than a cohort of physicians graduating to practice medicine has an answer which is less clear. There is no good reason to assume it is so, and several theoretical reasons suggest it would definitely not be so. At least, not unless the nurses had somehow been hand-picked for the job, based on prior experience—but then, the comparison would only be fair if the physicians were also similarly hand-picked. All of this is fraught with difficulty in our union-dependent environment.

The question of who does a better job turns out to be less important than the conditions under which each expects to work. Doctors expect, for the most part, to be at least partly entrepreneurial in their practice and to pay for their own overhead and practice costs. They are also trained to make judgements rather than follow protocols someone else has set. The traditions in nursing are quite different. Nurses tend to want protocols to follow, are not trained to make judgements that involve risk, and prefer to work in a salaried environment in which an employer pays all set-up costs and accepts ultimate responsibility—if not for individual patients, then at least for the operation as a whole.

These are not necessarily unworkable requirements, but there is not a tradition in Canada of government-operated clinics employing nurses as primary care workers. That is not to say it has not been tried. It has, but even when the push is given, the ultimate direction of such a project has never been clear. For one thing, the costs of the operation, when all overhead is included, have always exceeded initial expectations and are greater than the alternative, which is to simply let physicians staff their own offices in the old, entrepreneurial fashion. For another, nurses who do such work tend to want to be paid more than their counterparts, who simply carry out doctors' orders.

Even when the project has started out with adequate funds and adequate organization, it is not clear that patients would choose such an arrangement over the option of having direct access to their own physician. For the most part, as long as the alternative of having a physician is there, they do not—a point which has smothered even the best-funded and well-intentioned project. Of course, the death blow at the moment to the nurse practitioner model is the current shortage of nurses. Even if one wanted to do it, there are not enough nurses to do it without offering a wage differential that would undermine the viability of the project.

The bottom line is not so much a question of whether nurses could do it as whether there is an economic need to fill. If there is, then the service will evolve against all obstacles, but if not, no amount of political correctness or resolve will make it thrive. Anyone who doubts this small wisdom should compare the dismal progress of the nurse practitioners with the growth of walk-in clinics. Here is an activity discouraged by governments, by traditional general practitioners, by consultants, by hospitals, and even by the doctors' own professional associations. By conventional calculations, walk-in clinics should have disappeared long ago, and yet they thrive while other traditional delivery systems suffer. The reason is that they do have the support of only one group, and that happens to be the only group that really counts—the consumers. The short answer is that, if people want nurse practitioners, they will be there. If not, no amount of organizational influence will make it happen.

The Future of Nursing

If this is a caring profession, then these are hard times for nurses. Contemplating absurd workloads, minimal recognition, and decreasing satisfaction from their patient-care duties, balanced with the demands of the personal challenges associated with middle age, one could be excused for being a pessimist.

On the other hand, if things look bleak now, it can only be a harbinger of better things to come. Nurses have proven their abilities and could easily take on more complex jobs, if they were willing to give up other things and if their own associations would let them. One thing is for sure, nurses no longer need to carry an inferiority complex about their role in the health-care industry. If nothing else, the experience of doing without nurses during the shortages has driven home how much they are needed, and how important their role has become.

Nursing today is much more than the Florence Nightingale image would suggest. Nurses have become indispensable drivers within nearly every aspect of our health system. They have more than proven their rightful place.

One more observation: nurses are on the brink of a substantial increase in pay, through one means or another. In part, this is a direct result of the economics of the nursing shortage. At the same time, it is recognition in a sense of their valuable contribution. No one will cheer as loudly as the doctors—one thing the shortage has taught them is the extent to which they rely on nurses in the first place. The days of rivalry between nurses and doctors are nearing a close, and the age when parallel professions are simply forced to cooperate is nearly upon us. Partly this is a generational thing. New graduates of medical school have a much higher regard for nurses than the previous generation, because they have seen them in action in settings which inspire professional respect. Perhaps with the relaxing of tensions between nurses and doctors, nurses will shed much of the self-imposed work they have voluntarily taken on. Perhaps they can evolve a more flexible professional organization, one that helps them move forward instead of holding them back. Perhaps.

THE MANAGERS

Too often we forget that systems do not run by themselves. Whether we like them or hate them, managers in one form or other are a vital ingredient in any large industry. Health care is no different, in that sense, from any other industry. Managers can be found throughout hospitals, at various levels in the hierarchies of the Health Authorities that spend health dollars, and in the provincial ministries that operate as an arm of government and distribute those dollars in the first place.

It is typical of those who work in the clinical fields of health care to underestimate the contribution of managers. They see them, at best, as a waste of resources that might be going into "real" services, and at worst, managers are seen as a malicious process, multiplying without purpose, and creating added confusion in an already stressed system. Let's face it—there are good managers and there are bad managers, but any large system that has to hire and fire people, buy goods and equipment, and account for the money spent, cannot function without them.

In Canada, management in the health field is plagued by a few endemic problems. When a doctor makes a mistake, it usually affects just one patient at a time. But when a manager makes a mistake, the consequences can be widespread, long-standing, and very expensive or even impossible to turn around. Managers have tremendous power to influence things in either direction, good or bad. But the people involved are not demons—simply people like anyone else, trying to do the best they can with what they have to work with. Before harbouring any resentment toward these individuals, it would be wise to understand what sort of system-wide problems they have to deal with.

The "Nolan Principle" of Management

One of the more enlightening moments in my education about management theory is one that I owe to Nolan Baynes, a one-time chief executive officer of the BC Ambulance Service. I have named it in his honour.

Nolan was a retired RCMP superintendent who had been parachuted in to provide some much-needed direction and discipline (as the Deputy Minister of Health at the time saw it) to the BC ambulance service. At the time, the service operated as an arm of the ministry of health and controlled, quite literally, all the ambulance services for the entire province. Exactly what someone with a career in the RCMP knew about ambulances was quite beyond the rest of us, but we were prepared to give the new CEO a chance.

As it turned out, Nolan was an amicable person, highly disciplined in his own demeanour, but very approachable, and one who didn't mind a bit if his staff addressed him by his first name. He became legendary for his clean desktop, a testament to his belief in delegating authority, and a deliberate reminder to others that he could keep a managerial eye on the proverbial forest instead of the trees. The approach made him popular with the managers who reported directly to him. He was fond of reminding us that, "If you can't write it on one page, don't bother sending it anywhere—no one will read it." The statement was slightly amusing but also seen as being brutally true. As if to anticipate our question, he would frequently explain that management was a science in itself, and that if you could master the science, managing one thing was not that different from managing something else. Nolan quickly gained a reputation for keeping things simple and for telling it like it was.

One day, over lunch in the cafeteria, he remarked to me that the service would be revamping their crew reports—the forms upon which ambulance attendants recorded the events of each call. The purpose of the overhaul was to improve our information base and eliminate unnecessary work. At the time, I was the senior medical advisor to the service, reporting directly to the CEO, although I also maintained my clinical practice as an emergency physician. My job put me in charge of and responsible for all the medical aspects of the ambulance service's work. I was thrilled at the prospect of finally improving our data systems and did not try to hide my enthusiasm.

"That's wonderful!" I exclaimed. "I've been pushing for this for a long time. We need a better database to know where we are effective and what we need to change." At the time, I had pioneered a computer database for tracking paramedic calls, and was the only one in the service using computerized data to make management decisions. Considering this was the early 1980s, this was no mean feat, but I knew there were limits to the quality of the data available, and was excited at the prospect of adding better information and using it on a wider scale.

"No, that's not exactly what I mean," Nolan added slowly, with a sombre tone. I calmed down quickly and listened more intently. "Fred here is in charge of changing the management side of the form—names, crew information, and so on." I nodded. I had no problem with Fred doing that. "But," Nolan continued, "we're going to cut back on the clinical part of the form and replace it simply with three checks—cardiac, trauma, or other."

My jaw dropped. How could he throw away all of our existing medical information? How could he not see this as an opportunity to increase, not decrease, the clinical information we were capturing? What he was suggesting went against all of the current experience in the field and would render us virtually blind to what our crews were achieving. I began to protest, but he continued.

"Actually, that's not exactly what we're going to do. It's just the starting point. Whenever we make a major change like this, it's important to wipe the slate clean and start from the beginning," he continued, with an earnest look meeting my gaze directly. "You're the medical advisor. Of course, you'll have an opportunity to tell us why it should not be so, and what exactly you would suggest."

I relaxed a little. It wasn't as horrible as I had first thought. But I was still sweating. I had been the medical director for almost ten years, and was generally credited with the progress in paramedic services. I was known nationally for this work and was one of the leaders in the improvement of ambulance services for the rest of Canada. Other provinces asked me for advice, and I was frequently asked to speak at conferences on the subject of ambulance services. Why had I suddenly lost credibility in my own back yard?

"But Nolan," I asked, "you know my track record. I devised the current form and the computer database that goes with it. I'm the only one in the service currently using computer information to make decisions. I'm recognized nationally for what I know about ambulance services in general. Why are you making me do this? Why can't you just listen to what I say?"

Nolan was quick to reply. "Yes, I know you're the architect of the current system, and I'm not saying I won't do what you say. You will have an opportunity next week to tell me whatever you like. It's the format that's important. You are the advisor. You give advice. I'm the manager. I make the decisions."

I was still incredulous. "Have I ever given you bad advice before?" I wanted to know.

"It's not that," he answered. "You are the expert, and experts can't be allowed to make decisions because they are always biased. The reason I make the decisions is because I'm not biased."

"Wait a minute," I muttered. "Just because I know something about this, that makes me biased?" I couldn't believe what I was hearing. At the same time, the force of the logic was compelling.

"Yes," he answered, "anyone who has information is always biased. That's why experts can never be trusted to make decisions. Experts are supposed to give their advice, but you need someone who is unbiased to actually make the decision."

"And that means someone who knows nothing about the problem?" I asked.

"Someone who *starts out* knowing nothing," he corrected. "But if the advisors are doing their job, he should eventually have all the information he needs to make the decision. Of course, the onus is on the advisors to make sure they say what's important. That's why you can have several advisors giving different advice, but only one decision-maker."

I could see the discussion was closed, and that was the way it was. I wasn't so worried about the forms any more, because I knew I would have a chance to make my arguments and I believed that Nolan would listen. The conversation had been a revelation to me. Suddenly I could see that not only Nolan believed it—so did many others. In fact, the more I looked around in public management, the more I recognized Nolan's logic in action.

My presentation the following week went well, but I left at the end of day feeling depressed. "Why do I feel so depressed?" I wondered to myself. "Everything I planned went my way." Nolan had liked my presentation and agreed to implement all of my suggestions. Then I realized why I was so depressed. All that time and effort, the week spent preparing my submission, and my day of presentations, had effectively been an exercise in treading water. We were no further ahead.

From that day on, I saw Nolan's principle of management behind almost every aspect of public service. There were a few exceptions, of course, but they were relatively rare. I realized that Nolan had helped me at least to explain what I was seeing, and for that I should be thankful.

But the theory was disturbing to me. If people who knew things were inherently biased and could not be trusted, that meant that decisions would always be made by people who knew little or nothing about the matter they were deciding. Advisors could never be perfect in what information they supplied, and even if they could, I knew people often misunderstood what they heard, or reached limits in the sheer amount of information they could comprehend. I was convinced that the system of advising the decision-maker was a guarantee of mediocrity in the long run, if not outright disaster. Perhaps this was the reason many health boards were specifically excluding doctors from membership. My own experience told me that successful groups were those who could select anyone they thought knew the most as a manager, and then let that person run with their decisions.

If our obsession as Canadians with avoiding bias meant keeping those with knowledge away from decision-making positions, it seemed to me that we were heading for trouble. But I was young at the time—it took a few more years to confirm my suspicions.

The Brain Drain

One of the major problems our managers face is similar to the one our professionals face—if it is important to have the best people as managers, we should value the ones who demonstrate ability. Our obsession with treating everyone as equally as possible is especially damaging to our public managers. Their pay is more closely scrutinized than that of other workers, and any significant spread between what we pay managers and what we pay the ones they manage is held as evidence of corruption. The press seems very quick in Canada to take these stories and publicize them as exposés of either favouritism or greed.

They forget that for years we have limited the increases in pay that managers in the public service receive until it is now not uncommon for them to receive the same, or less, than what their subordinates receive. We also consistently overlook the extra hours and time flexibility that managers need to complete their work. If all that time were counted, the hourly rate would be much lower than what their subordinates receive. The common explanation is that this is only just—since managers have a "better" job, they should not also receive more pay. Alternatively, the moral imperative is invoked, of being a contributor to the community, and that it is too crass to want to be paid extra for something that should be a public duty.

Regardless of the moral persuasions, the evidence is overwhelming that failing to reward people with pay eventually means they leave. Nowhere is that consequence more painfully felt than in our public service. Besides low pay and low esteem from others, our public managers are punished with excessive workloads, lack of recognition, and are often forced to work for people who know less than they do. Ultimately, our public servants are subjected to the worst indignity of all—subservience to the political agenda. No wonder so many of them leave. Even the ones who willingly accept less pay than they could earn in the private sector cannot work without autonomy from political interference and without an opportunity to see some fruit for their labours.

The combination of the brain drain in our public service with Nolan's principle has had a devastating effect on our trusted civil service. It has guaranteed that it is not competence that is rewarded, but faithfulness. The most competent ones get driven out, and those that remain faithful to the team (or perhaps have less prospect of getting another job) remain. Guess who stays around to get the promotion.

I don't mean to say that all of our managers in public service are incompetent. On the contrary, we are fortunate in Canada to still have many dedicated individuals who are highly capable and believe in public service to the point where they are willing to forgo the greater rewards of private enterprise. It is just that these people tend not to get rewarded, either by pay or by recognition for what they do. After years of dedicated service, many of them get tired of never seeing any positive results from their labour and eventually leave. Is this any way to reward people for the dedication they show?

Remember Who the Boss Is

Most people who enter the public service—whether as managers, or clerks, or doctors, or nurses—do so because they want to help society, and find a rewarding and meaningful career for themselves at the same time. It isn't until much later that they become jaded and take out their frustrations on the job.

We still have this myth in Canada that, while politicians are the titular head of their ministries, it is the full-time bureaucrats who really know the business and make all the important decisions. It is a reassuring fantasy, but quite untrue. It is, in fact, the politicians who make the money decisions in any ministry—especially health—and politics run the ministry. Management staff may try their best to run their portfolios on a businesslike footing, but those who survive in government quickly learn their priorities. There are only two: (a) balance your budget for the current year, and (b) protect your minister—not necessarily in that order.

My first lesson on the power of the minister came during my first week in the offices of the Ministry of Health of British Columbia. As a young physician consultant, I must have looked particularly vulnerable and naïve that day. One of the more senior physicians in the ministry, who was then the Director of Hospital Programs, called me into his office and asked me to shut the door. It didn't take long for him to come to the point.

"If you want to last around here, you'll have to learn one thing. Don't ever say those words within earshot of the minister." He was referring to the name of the hospital I worked in. "He can't stand that hospital." My ears buzzed at the words. I was well known as an innovator and a leader in many aspects of medicine. Had I already been careless and violated the taboo? I thought perhaps I had, and that was the reason for the lesson.

I might have put two and two together, because the doctors at this particular hospital had recently gone public with their displeasure about ministerial policies. But did that mean no one could mention the name? Was this any way to run a multi-billion-dollar industry, not to mention one with a public humanitarian mission?

If the news startled me, imagine the effect it had on the people who worked in the ministry and were trying to do a reasonable job for the public's benefit. Some could not stomach the working conditions and simply left, but many—either unable or unwilling to do that—simply accepted the state of affairs as something that had to be tolerated. Whatever it did for morale, it did much more to limit the potential and the effectiveness of the ministry itself. It is a common frustration with front-line workers that the management staff they must report to are to be blamed for much of the ills of the system. What they fail to understand is that anyone forced to work under a set of nonsense rules will eventually begin to appear incompetent to those on the outside.

Fads in Healthcare

Perhaps it is only human nature, but just as fads dominate fashion, music, education, and the automobile industry, health care has its own set of fads that dominate for a few years, then fall by the way-side. At the time, each seems to be "the answer" to a host of problems and is taken up almost like mob psychology. In a sense, understanding the fads goes a long way toward explaining why we have come to this place and why we are not alone. Fads, by their very nature—once they take hold—convince a lot of people all at the same time. The management staff who try to rationalize health care in Canada are no exception, so without necessarily any malice toward them, we will try to look at a few of these fads, especially those which have taken hold in Canada over the last several years.

1. THE HMO FAD

The Health Maintenance Organization, or HMO, is now a common entity, found mostly in the U.S. The concept is better known more recently by the euphemism "managed care," and is now much-reviled for its tendency to restrict both patients and doctors from the treatments and actions that they know are required. Perhaps so, but many people may be surprised to know that the movement had its beginnings in socialized medicine.

Since the 1960s, when government tinkering with health care became big business, the fee-for-service method of payment for doctors' services has been a concern. Part of this was an economic concern that doctors were able to pad their lab-coats by charging fees whenever people were ill enough to be seen. Part of it was a prevention-oriented concern that doctors were only rewarded for making people sick, not for making them better. It became a popular notion that if doctors could make people either sick or healthy, they should rather be rewarded for doing the latter than the former. Instead of paying doctors per visit, then, they were to be paid up front for 'signing up' patients while healthy. If they stayed healthy, the doctor would have less work to do, but would still be paid the same amount. Therein lay the incentive. The pay stayed the same (and could, under some schemes, be quite generous), but the work varied. Successful doctors, therefore, were those who could keep people healthy, having already collected their generous fees in advance.

Like all partial truths, the idea had its attractive aspects. The trouble was, the other way to be 'successful' was to simply choose a patient base that was known to be low-risk. It was for this reason that many people with chronic illness or a family history of disease had difficulty finding care. There were other problems, too. For example, another way to be 'successful' was to limit the services offered once people did in fact get sick. Since much of medicine is practiced without clear consensus, paying agencies could pick and choose treatment regimes that were less expensive but still within the bounds of accepted medical practice, at least among some physicians. In particular, many large insurance companies in the U.S. who had become very good at assessing risk, saw it as a way of making money.

Soon, the rules had become excessively rigid and medical practitioners who worked in managed care settings found they were barred from doing certain tests and procedures on their patients, often for frivolous or bureaucratic reasons. Often the insurance companies (in the U.S.) that owned the HMO employed people with only high school graduation to enforce the regulations, which pitted experienced physicians against non-medical people who had no grasp of the real complexity behind the rules they were trying to enforce. The turning point in the industry is only just occurring as the consumers themselves (the patients) have taken heed of the restrictions placed on their physicians, and even on seeing certain physicians, and have begun to vote with their feet. As HMOs see their revenues dwindling along with their client base, they are being forced to re-evaluate their policies.

Indeed, the more forward thinking of the HMOs are now understanding that the money they spent policing doctors has not only cost them by driving away clients, it has failed to save any money in the first place. In over 98 percent of cases, the tests were eventually done anyway, just as the doctors initially requested, and the savings did not even begin to pay for the salaries of those hired to do the policing. It turns out that what the doctor ordered was, under the circumstances, usually just what was really required.

What does this have to do with Canada? For one thing, the idea of "maintaining health," by large-scale intervention in how doctors are paid and with a captive client base, is a natural for the architects of Canadian medicare. Putting doctors on salary has long been, for some, part of the medicare agenda—one that remains, except in certain pockets of practice, largely unfulfilled. But a global budget for hospitals is in itself a form of 'salary' for the institution. In many ways, Canada's health system operates as one big HMO—at least, as far as the facilities and hospitals are concerned. The health budget is the same, no matter how much work needs to be done. The owner, instead of an insurance company, is the government, but the rule-making process is just as restrictive. Instead of rules enforced by high school graduates, the restrictions are budgetary and organizational: no, this hospital may not have a CT scanner, since there is already one at the neighbouring hospital only 20 miles away. No, that community may not have a cardiac surgical unit—it may continue to refer its cardiac patients to the university centre only 300 miles away. It is cheaper to offer an air ambulance to ferry the patients back and forth than to pay for a whole new cardiac unit.

There is one big difference, though, between managed care in the U.S. and in Canada. Eventually, in the U.S., individual consumers can still choose whether to support one health scheme or another. Whether the user pays directly, or his insurance company pays for him, or whether the federal Medicare money follows him, his decision to cross the street gives a powerful message to the HMO that loses his business. Unlike the parent who railed against the administrators in the vignette at the beginning of my earlier chapter about *The Hospitals*, there is a consequence to his anger in the U.S. In Canada, whether we like the HMO operated by the government or not, we are not allowed any other legal options. Canadians cannot choose a different HMO.

2. THE PREVENTION FAD

This is one of the more enduring fads that came on the heels of the HMO concept itself. If we can prevent illness, then certainly it is better to do that than treat an established disease. Apart from the financial incentives to the doctor, everyone knows that an ounce of prevention is worth a pound of cure. Instead of spending money treating disease, we should be spending money to prevent it. What could be more humanitarian, as well as fiscally responsible, than that?

No one should take my remarks as evidence that I am opposed to prevention. Without question, some of the greatest advances in medicine—including aseptic technique, vaccination, and a host of public health measures such as sewage control—benefit more people than almost any other specific treatment. The issue is not whether we should invest in prevention or not. Clearly we must. It is whether it can, to any appreciable extent, take the place of acute care.

Some things lend themselves well to prevention. Seat belts really do decrease injuries and death from car accidents. Safety caps really do prevent accidental poisonings in children. Stopping smoking really does decrease the risk of heart and lung disease. But some things seem difficult or impossible to prevent. Diabetes, with all of its long-term complications, eludes our efforts to find a cause, never mind prevent it. Most forms of cancer, although we can learn how to decrease the odds, seem to follow the rules of a throw of dice as much as anything else. Some things as widespread as alcohol abuse and its consequences—both social and medical—seem to defy our efforts at prevention, and even control is an uphill battle. I could go on, but the point is a simple one: not everything is preventable.

To make matters more complicated, even preventive behaviour itself can have adverse consequences. Physical activity, for example, is widely accepted as a way of preventing heart and lung illness, but carries its own cost in terms of accidents and joint injury. For the most part, some illness seems to be a fact of life.

And yet, it is extremely difficult for humans to accept that something is inevitable, that under certain circumstances there is nothing we can do to safeguard ourselves. Accepting that level of loss of control seems to go against our human instincts.

Even when we have an effective measure for prevention, many of the proven effective strategies take a long time to implement and even longer before we see a benefit. Smoking, for example, was suspected as a cause of lung cancer during the late 1950s. It wasn't until the 1990s that anti-smoking laws became widespread, and the smoking rate is only now beginning to decrease in this country. The lung cancer rate in the meantime is still booming, because it takes 20 years for cancer to develop from its cellular beginnings into a clinical entity. Even seat-belt legislation and helmet laws have taken a decade or more to become established in most jurisdictions. The benefits of exercise have been known for decades, but it is only now that the yuppie generation has made aerobics something that fits into the workplace. When we will see an actual cost-saving effect of widespread improvements in fitness is anybody's guess.

My point is simply this: prevention is important for those health problems where it works, but even then, it can take decades to pay off. Some things we must accept as beyond our ability to prevent. No matter what, prevention is never an alternative to providing care. It is an add-on that will bring its payoffs much later on, if indeed it pays off at all. It seems like an obvious point, but in the budget pressure of modern governments, any excuse to cut budgets looks pretty attractive, especially when people without any knowledge of the industry make the decisions.

Health care in Canada has suffered greatly at the sacred altar of prevention. Money and resources have been allocated, sometimes with little proof of effectiveness, often at the expense of proven treatment for existing disease. No one would have deliberately designed it so, but in the helter-skelter of a system that is politically directed and already running out of money, we sometimes use one arm to hurt another.

3. THE ANTI-DOCTOR FAD

Quite contrary to the benevolent doctor image described in a previous chapter, a large number of people actually see doctors as villains. Some accuse them of elitism with respect to others in the health care industry (especially nurses), and of making exorbitant incomes. While it is not a crime in Canada to make a lot of money, it does not exactly engender public empathy, either.

But I am not talking about the popular form of mistrust, which might be directed at anyone who makes more money than they "should." I want to talk about a fad which accuses doctors of a different form of villainy—namely, of deliberately driving up health-care costs. This is accomplished (so the argument goes) in two ways. First, doctors charge fees that are beyond what other workers make, even with comparable training. Secondly, they push the fee-for-service system by making patients visit more often than necessary. Even if they cannot directly do anything about it, governments display their resentment against this power that doctors wield by using accusatory language in media releases, especially around the time when contracts are being negotiated. The practice of publishing the amount of money doctors receive from medicare each year (even though they are acknowledged to be only gross incomes from which expenses must be paid) is blatant evidence that this resentment about remuneration in general is still an issue.

Aside from the accusations of abuse, there is no doubt that doctors cost the system, because they perform activities that cost money. No one is disputing that someone with appendicitis needs their appendix out, but there are a host of medical and surgical activities, not to mention costly investigations, that some say simply do not "need to be done." The evidence presented to support the contention that a particular procedure (call it procedure X) is really unnecessary is of three types:

(1) Lack of measurable benefit on the health of the population.

(2) Not all doctors in the community follow the same practices, so if Dr. A never does procedure X under a certain set of conditions, why should Dr. B?

(3) If procedure X is performed much less often in another country without any apparent ill effects, why should we do it more often here?

The cost to the public system of unnecessary procedures could potentially be enormous, depending of course on whether the procedures labelled "unnecessary" really are or not. For example, one common contention is that too many gallbladder surgeries are being done. Gallbladder disease is not a life-threatening disorder and many people can live for years without experiencing an attack. Cholecystectomy (the operation to remove the gallbladder) rates in England are approximately half what they are in Canada and no one seems to be dying there or complaining of gallbladder torture. It seems a small leap in logic to therefore conclude doctors here are recommending cholecystectomy to twice as many people as really need it done, presumably so they can collect the fees associated with the procedure.

One way of solving the "unnecessary procedure" problem would be to abolish fee-for-service altogether and replace it with some form of capitation fee (as described in the previous chapter). Since that would eliminate the profit potential of doing another gallbladder operation, the surgery would only represent more work, so doctors would therefore only do it when they had to (i.e., when the patient really needed it, which is assumed to be the same thing).

Another way to solve the problem would be to limit the number of doctors allowed to practice. To put it simply, when governments looked during the 1980s for "causes" of high expenses, they found that costs were directly related to the number of doctors practicing in an area. As ridiculous as this sounds, limiting the number of practicing doctors by restricting billing numbers was actually a mainstream action for most provincial governments about 15 years ago. To make the decrease in the number of physicians more durable, the federal government moved within a few years to drastically decrease medical school enrollments across the country. Now, a decade or more later—precisely at the time when these actions are finally showing their effects—we have an acknowledged doctor shortage lurking over us. Suddenly, governments are positioning themselves on the defender side of health care and talking about increasing medical school enrollments, but not one elected politician has acknowledged the error which contributed to the shortage in the first place. These actions were deliberate and done without apology. Our elected officials at the time truly felt this level of intervention was necessary to balance the damage from unrestrained market forces. And yet, the argument about unnecessary procedures is a compelling one. Is it true?

There is no question that unnecessary procedures are sometimes done. The question is, how big is the problem and does its size warrant drastic intervention? The sad truth is that there is no consensus on much of medical practice, and what consensus does exist is subject to frequent change as evidence from controlled trials continually comes in. If we compare two different doctors' practices and find one does fewer procedure Xs than the other, the one that does more is just as likely to be "correct"—forcing the lower one always to be the gold standard is a dangerous practice. Furthermore, always insisting on a statistically valid proof of benefit is fraught with errors as well. Most statistics look at nothing more sophisticated than age-adjusted death rates. Gallbladder attacks, for example, rarely cause death but cause a good deal of misery and absence from work. We simply do not have the information needed to statistically measure this kind of outcome on a mass scale. We also know that the incidence of specific diseases varies widely from community to community and country to country, and blindly choosing the country with the most favourable statistic and applying that to our own country is hardly worthy of being called science. The reasons are attributed to dietary or cultural differences but the real causes are not known.

It has long been known, for example, that Chinese living in Asia have a much higher rate of oesophageal cancer than those in North America, but a lower rate of cancer of the lower bowel. We conjecture that dietary roughage has something to do with it, but we really don't know. What is clear is that we cannot simply compare procedures across continents and expect to get something useful.

In the end, we must leave individual decisions to individuals, and allow the doctor assigned to each case to make his/her decision. Not all decisions are right, but not all second-guessing is right, either.

Does it mean we have to throw up our hands and abandon any thought of controlling a potentially costly and dangerous practice? Not at all. But we must recognize that quality control in medicine is an ongoing activity that already takes place between doctors, and is not improved when imposed by politicians or bureaucrats. Many 'practice protocols' have been developed already, and more are accumulating every year, that represent consensus among physicians about how certain diseases should be handled, with ways to measure compliance. Practice protocols recognize that each patient should be treated as an individual but that overall patterns can and should be tracked. In this way, they allow the best of both worlds—an individual approach to each patient, based on the merits of the case, and consensus to narrow the amount of overall variation that occurs from one physician to another in the treatment of similar cases. Research shows that the practice protocol method works both to decrease costs (by decreasing the amount of variation) and to improve quality of care (because they become important teaching and feedback tools to physicians). They are not overnight fixes, though, and they don't support any particular political philosophy. Too bad.

4. The Amalgamation Fad

Another way to reduce costs is to amalgamate existing institutions. Doctors are not the only ones who are seen as "bad" characters in the game of health care. Institutions (i.e., hospitals) and the individuals (especially managers) who run them are also seen as potential problems, through empire-building. It is only natural, after all, for hospital administrators to want to increase their power base by expanding what their hospital owns and does. Even if there is no direct financial reward, it is one way of showing success and claiming "bragging rights." Whatever the motivation, financial structures are carefully tuned to discourage or prevent outright any such thing. Even if there are no villains at all, it is easy to show that amalgamating certain services can generate savings. Instead of two accounting departments, only one is needed. The same is true for laundry, personnel services, and so on. The fact that each department does twice as much without an increase in pay is not generally a limiting consideration.

So amalgamations perform two functions: one is a true saving by reduction in support staff, and the other is an undermining of the possibility for individual empire-building. True savings are sometimes made when critical mass is achieved that enables certain technical changes, such as better computer systems—but in general, the reason for amalgamation is generally encompassed in one word: rationalization.

"Rationalization" is the term used to answer the question, "Why should we have two of something when one will do?" If two hospitals are a mile apart from each other, why do both have to have neurosurgery units? One hospital could take all the neurosurgery for the area, while the other takes, for example, all of the orthopaedics. The reduction in staff produces a savings and the care actually improves because the activity level is higher within each service, thereby improving experience and efficiency.

One can understand the appeal. The very term implies that anything else is "not rational." During the mid-'80s, Toronto General Hospital and Toronto Western Hospital merged (were forced by government to merge, to put it more precisely) as a way of saving money. The boards and administrators were amalgamated, and complete medical departments were swapped to "avoid duplication." Some jobs became redundant, but with one common administration, the hospitals would cooperate seamlessly to offer not the same, but even better care—or so the theory went.

The reality was somewhat different. Staff loyalty to their own institution was hit hard. Patients requiring two or more services at the same time (such as traumatic accident victims) were left in uncertainty while staff decided whether it was better to shuttle the patient or the service to the other hospital. Even though the distance between institutions was less than a mile, the logistics of actually doing the transfers was much worse than expected, with rush-hour traffic playing an increasingly frustrating role. Publicly, the government declared the experiment a success. Privately, staff were outraged at the additional pressure with which they had to deal and the impossibility of providing reasonable care under those conditions.

Whatever the outcome, the practice of merging hospitals has caught on like wildfire in all provinces. Although there may well be strategic advantages with true savings in some mergers, these were political convenience mergers that paid little regard to the logistics involved. Some of the other fads have died a natural death, but this one lives on. Hospital administrators are not, after all, in a position to voice views that do not support those of their ministry of health. Those who see it differently are not around long enough to listen to the commentary, and penalties imposed on the budgets of dissenting hospitals are legendary. Mergers save money, and the effect on patient care is imprecise enough that few people want to listen to all the arguments.

One long-term effect that was never anticipated is now surfacing, and will demand a larger share of attention in the near future. I call it the 'cockroach effect'. Cockroaches are notorious for their ability to survive. They have inhabited our earth essentially unchanged, we are told, for at least 400 million years. One of their more interesting characteristics is their ability to withstand nuclear radiation. The truth is that they are killed by radiation—just like any other living being—but they can survive huge doses. The lethal dose of radiation for a cockroach is about 100 times that for human beings (adjusted for body weight). The reason is not a special covering or clever protection, as was once thought, nor is their DNA structure different or fundamentally more resistant to radiation than ours. The real reason cockroaches survive that much radiation is because of one characteristic: redundancy. Radiation does not kill directly—it kills by damaging DNA so that cells that divide are unable to produce the required proteins. Cockroaches can have over 80 different chromosomes that produce the same protein. So even if some of the DNA is destroyed by radiation, there is enough redundancy in its chromosomes that it can just carry right along as if nothing had happened.

Just as redundancy gives the cockroach resistance to adverse events, so redundancy in hospital capabilities gives alternatives for patients when something goes wrong. So called "rationalization of services" in hospital care, then, is not really "rational" at all. It is simply trading away the stability that goes with redundancy for a short-term drop in costs. As the system becomes increasingly stressed to the limit—as is now frequently the case—patients who might have had other alternatives now have none. They have been done in by rationalization.

Rohmer's Law and the Gatekeeper Theory

Hardly a meeting of senior health-care administrators goes by without someone making a joke about Rohmer's Law. Even though no one seems to know who Rohmer is, or what the context of his famous statement was, his "law," like the classical urban myth, survives. Somewhat paraphrased, Rohmer's Law states that:

> *No matter what quantity of resources is provided,*
> *it will never be enough.*

It is no joke. Most health-care administrators either believe it, or use it as a cynical rationalization for their jobs. If we look across Canada, the "law" certainly appears to be true, in spite of the fact that it flies in the face of classical economics. The obvious question, whether it applies to anything else other than health care, is usually avoided. If it does, then the next natural question would be "What determines where the law applies and where it does not?" These, however, are semantic niceties that are usually ignored in those situations where *Rohmer's Law* is invoked. For our purposes, we can assume that the "law" was either drafted with health care in mind, or that it has negligible consequences elsewhere. The dangerous problem with Rohmer's Law is that, if it is true, then so is *Rohmer's Corollary*, which states that:

Since resources are never enough, then the act of further decreasing resources will have no discernible effect.

When one casts an eye at other systems as diverse as the U.S. and Bulgaria, it is clear that *Rohmer's Law* is not true. Many examples of unused hospital beds and staff can be found, often coexisting with shortages elsewhere. The cryptic answer to *Rohmer's Law*, then, which I call *Rohmer's Folly*, states that:

When shortages become severe, Rohmer's Law **appears to apply.**

Joke or not, *Rohmer's Law* describes quite clearly the Canadian reality for most managers and management staff who work in the health industry. They understand that they can never hope to achieve equilibrium between what the public wants and what the public purse can provide. That means that the entire thrust of their efforts is aimed at trying somehow to stem the tide of demands. The analogy of a "wall" is quite apt, between the available resources, if you like, and the wild hordes wanting access. If unrestrained, these public hordes would quickly deplete all the available resources, leaving the less aggressive needy with none. The job of the health-care administrator, therefore, is much like that of a gatekeeper—fending off the hordes and allocating available resources as fairly as possible.

The "gates" at which these gatekeepers concentrate their actions are the access points to the system—namely, hospital admission, operating rooms, and the emergency department. The sizes of the gates are regulated by the size of the respective budgets the ministries assign to the various hospitals. The actual 'manning' of the gates is cynically delegated to the physicians responsible for managing these departments.

That means that the clinical head of the emergency department in a particular hospital becomes responsible for keeping the number of patients admitted below the set value for that institution, regardless of who or what comes into the department. This gatekeeper role is assigned without that physician's necessarily agreeing to accept it, since it is inherently in conflict with the need to care for the patient, which is the primary responsibility of all physicians. And yet, these physicians have no choice but to accept the role, unless they decide not to practice that specialty.

Underlying the belief in the gatekeeper model is the conviction that there are always too many beds in the system and a significant number are occupied by people who do not really need them. The point was driven home by a study completed in 1998 at the University of British Columbia,[3] that concluded that almost 50 percent of patients occupying medical beds did not need to be in hospital. The study seemed to echo what many politicians and management staff already believed and gave more force to their determination to further limit access to hospital beds, even though the intent of the article had been misunderstood.

In fact, the fine print in the same article made the point that only one percent of the inpatients studied really did not need any care—the rest needed one or more services that could have been provided in an outpatient setting, *had one been available.* It also pointed out that the reason these people were still in hospital was that the services were *NOT* otherwise available, and also when more than one service was needed, the logistics of providing them outside of hospital became more costly than the in-hospital method. For example, some patients might have needed IV antibiotics, CT scans, and physiotherapy—each of which might have been, in theory, available to an outpatient—but the difficulties of scheduling and

[3] "Acute Medical Beds: How are they used in British Columbia?". A study conducted for the Advisory Committee on Clinical Resource Management. Ministry of Health BC. January 1997.

transporting an elderly patient to that many appointments would have exceeded the cost of the bed in the first place.

The persistent belief that there were too many hospital beds led to an attempt to reach agreement on how many beds were really needed in any given community. The real answer clearly depends on the incidence of disease in the community, and it is already well known this is dependent on factors such as age and socio-economic class, as well as incidence of underlying disorders such as diabetes, alcoholism, heart disease, etc. Rather than embark on a realistic estimate that took these factors into account, most health economists worked toward an overall average ratio of beds to population. As we saw in an earlier chapter, BC adopted a ratio of 2.75 beds per 1,000 population as their designated requirement in 1991. Privately, most economists admitted they did not know what the requirement was, and that it could only be realized by testing the waters, as it were, and seeing what happened. The notion that bed reductions took years to achieve and years to reverse (if, indeed, one could even find the nurses needed to reverse the situation once they had been laid off) was not one that seemed important at the time. Indeed, many communities have since seen their bed ratios drop below the magic level determined by British Columbia. The fact that no immediate reaction was apparent seemed to bolster the theory that reductions were, for all intents and purposes, a bottomless exercise and could go on almost forever.

The inherent clash between the pressure managers feel to maintain gatekeeper activity in their institutions and the gatekeeper roles assigned to reluctant physicians underlies a potential powder keg of animosity between these two groups of professionals, and plays an important part in producing and maintaining an atmosphere of distrust. That distrust makes co-operation, even on mutually agreeable projects, a source of difficulty. No wonder people make jokes about things like Rohmer's Law during meet-ings—the alternative would make the job unbearable.

The Managers Fight Back

As the examples above illustrate, our health care managers and management staff are as much victims in the medicare experiment as anyone else. They are unable to openly oppose their political masters without committing career suicide, but they can fight back in one sense. A host of non-profit societies are actively supporting research into management methods in health care. Together, they work to bring the rationality of science back to health care, in place of political bias.

Several medical journals (notably the prestigious *New England Journal of Medicine*) now routinely devote space on a regular basis to management issues, employing the same results-oriented approach as is currently used in medical research. Eventually, knowledge accumulates and so will expertise, because no one wants to repeat the mistakes of others.

In the end, like it or not, our managers are part of the health-care team. Things have simply become much too complex and technical for physicians and nurses to handle on their own. Most of the managers, if given the chance to do the work they wanted to do, would do credit to the system and to the staff and health pro-fessionals with whom they work, because they share our overall objectives. Their tie to the preoccupation about money of their political masters is a strained one—one that many would renounce if given an opportunity. Deep down inside, managers are no dif-ferent than anyone else in the health industry and they want to make a positive contribution. We owe them a chance to try.

THE PATIENTS

No discussion of the players in the health-care drama would be complete without a better understanding of the end users of health care, by which I mean the general public. What we do is, after all, a product of who we are. A proper analysis of all the characteristics of the public who make up our patients—or 'client base,' as the business types would call it—would be endless, and that is not our intent here. But a tremendous change in the makeup of our population is afoot, and ignoring that change would be foolish.

Demography Rules

The one thing everyone acknowledges is that we are all getting older. We are also living longer and having fewer children. According to Statistics Canada, the proportion of our population over the age of 65 was 9.4 percent in 1980, 11.9 percent in 1994, and 12.5 percent in 2000. As people age, they are more prone to disease and require more care. That 11.9 percent of the population accounted for 38.9 percent of our total health-care spending during 1994—more than three times the per person average, and more than 4.6 times the per person amount spent on their counterparts (those under 65).

In the meantime, the core of our social unit, the nuclear family, is taking a severe beating. It is a cruel irony that the name general practitioners chose for their association, the *College of Family Practice*, is in diametric opposition to one of our most pervasive social trends, the breakdown of the family unit. Single-parent families are becoming as common in many communities as the traditional two-parent family. Divorce rates have never been higher, and many people view common-law relationships, serial monogamy, and homosexual marriages as perfectly acceptable options.

People are also becoming more mobile. They tend to change jobs more often and are more likely to move to another community for reasons of career, marriage, or divorce. A mere fifty years ago, people rarely traveled more than a few kilometres from where they were born and lived. The ability to travel longer distances with ease, whether by car, bus, or airplane, has meant there are fewer obstacles to keep people from moving longer distances from their parents, siblings or children. The resulting effect on their support systems when times get tough is predictable, and the health system must accept much of that burden.

Much has also been written about the shorter attention span people have, induced presumably by the 30-minute pace of popular television in which problems are raised, recognized, and solved, all within the half-hour excluding commercial breaks. Fewer people read books (which take a relatively long time), and more are likely to watch TV, videos, or participate in mass entertainment events. Whatever the reason, people tend to be less patient about the things they want, and less loyal to brands they have always supported. Those in the marketing industry are well aware of this when they design their ads, always keeping in mind that their audience has itchy thumbs resting on their remote control units.

And finally, this is a population in Canada that has unprecedented access to information through mass media outlets, telephone, e-mail and Internet access. Canadians, among the earliest and most prolific users of the Internet and cellphones in the world, are also among the world's best educated in terms of basic literacy. Relative to many other countries, Canada has been a bountiful and safe place to live, free of war for the lifetime of most of its population, and privileged to be able to take issues of basic fairness, safety, and the rule of law for granted. Many in other countries would say Canadians have an easy go of life, without the dangers and hardships those in less-fortunate surroundings have had to endure.

That is our population, and out of that mix come our health care consumers and patients. Sometimes cast as passive recipients of whatever the government dishes out, the truth is, they are anything but passive. Even aside from the more vocal special interest groups that clamour for more of this or more of that, the public determines, to a large extent, how the incentives become distorted.

The only thing that is passive about the users is their general ignorance of how the system is designed to work and what is reasonably expected of them. Otherwise, patients behave in a way very similar to other consumer groups: they do what is best for themselves.

The Lure of Alternative Medicine

Considering the financial restrictions under which conventional medicine is forced to operate, the growth of alternative forms of free-market, health-oriented care is truly astounding, supported voluntarily by the same people who are so vigorously protected from user fees by government. By alternative medicine, I include all the parallel industries to traditional medical doctors and hospitals. These include the health food industry, herbal medicines, chiropractors, massage therapists, psychologists, and everything else from holistic medical practitioners to phrenologists. Whether alternative medicine works or not is quite irrelevant. People with free choice are willing to pay for it, and in economic terms, this establishes its value—something traditional medicine is unable to do.

A study published in the *Journal of the American Medical Association* in November 1998, showed that the number of people using at least one of 16 alternative therapies studied had increased from 34 to 42 percent during the years from 1990 to 1997. That represents a 25 percent increase, not only in the absolute quantity of alternative medicine being consumed, but in the proportion of the population that chose alternatives to conventional medicine.

One of the major medical journals in Canada[4] published a scoring system in a 1998 article that compared conventional and "unorthodox" practitioners on a set of parameters such as "length of time with patient," amount of touching involved, listening to the patient, and emotional satisfaction. It should be no surprise that conventional medicine was an inferior product with respect to every one of the qualities listed. Somehow, we expect that the rationality of traditional medicine should win some points, but the sheer weight of the advantages enjoyed by alternative medicine is impressive (see Table, opposite).

So, what is the truth about traditional medicine? Quite simply, the sheer breadth of different techniques and disciplines makes it impossible to be sure what is going on in any one area, or even to compare specific disciplines. What we do know is that conventional medicine rests on a tradition that insists on scientific proof. This means that before a particular treatment is accepted, its superiority over the alternatives—including the option of doing nothing—must meet at least three criteria:

---

[4] ML Bridgen, Annals Royal College of Physicians and Surgeons of Canada, Vol 31, No. 1, Feb 1998, by permission.

Differences Patients Perceive Between Conventional and Unorthodox Therapists (from ML Bridgen)

PERCEIVED QUALITY	CONVENTIONAL PRACTITIONER	UNORTHODOX PRACTITIONER
Time	May be rushed; average 6 to 10 minutes per patient	Un-rushed; average 90 min. for first consultation, 20 min per follow-up
Setting	May be depersonalized and institutionalized	Effort made for patient's comfort and personalization
Continuity	Patient may see different person on follow-up visits	Patient usually sees same person
Symptom handling	Trained to interpret symptoms in light of knowledge of underlying disease	Accepts patient's symptoms at face value
Emotional handling	Empathic abilities may be lacking	Empathic abilities central to therapist's skill
Dealing with patient's uniqueness	May try to compensate for or minimize personal idiosyncrasies of patient	Therapist regards patient's personal features as central to illness, treatment
Dealing with social context	Variable; importance of social context may be ignored or underestimated	Social context regarded as central to understanding of illness
Appearance of certainty	May seem uncertain; must express both sides of controversy regarding therapy	Certain and confident; testimonials point to 100 per cent success rate
Ability to give a clear prognosis	Obliged to be statistically accurate; may seem unclear or unintelligible	Free to deceive usually provides clear and optimistic prognosis
Ability to provide hope	Variable; may not be a component of therapeutic relationship	Usually a major part of the therapeutic relationship

(a) It must be reproducible by others who reach the same conclusion

(b) It must meet criteria defined ahead of time, before the experiment, and

(c) The results must be clear enough to convince a 'blinded' observer in a clinical trial.

Criterion (c) refers to research in which the treatment is actually tried and compared to alternatives (including placebo), and the results observed by judges who do not know which patients got the real treatment. This process of "blinding" is the key to the scientific method, because it is the only way to be sure none of the choices are due to bias—conscious or not. The rules of conventional science are that the numbers of people tested and the repetition of success must be such that the bounds of chance are exceeded by a statistical probability of 1 in 20. That means that a treatment that has passed the "scientific method" has been repeatedly tested and found to be better than an alternative, and to doing nothing, and that the assessments were done by people who did not know who was really treated and that the chances of the result being a random one are less than 1 in 20. These are rigorous criteria and costly to meet. Although not everything in traditional medicine has passed such rigorous testing, the list grows every day, as thousands of studies are carried out and subjected to peer critique in the medical literature.

Few people can argue with these principles, yet alternative medicine owes no such allegiance to any blinded testing or scientific process. It is based, instead, on a series of mostly personal testimonials, and sometimes on vested interests. Does this mean none of it works? Of course not. It is hard to imagine that none of the techniques practiced for decades or more are not at least occasionally useful. Surely some personal experiences and testimonials are perfectly valid. The problem is, there is no way to know which ones are and which are not. In the field of alternative medicine, the age-old adage of *caveat emptor* seems to be particularly apt.

To be fair, many of the current practitioners of alternative medicine are attempting to copy the scientific method of testing and adapt it to their own field. The problem is, intent is one thing, but ensuring that trials are truly without bias is not a simple task. Also, some therapies do not lend themselves well to blinding. Imagine trying to test massage therapy by blinding the patients to whether they were massaged or not. Besides the clinical trials themselves, a mountain of work would be required simply to bring the terminology in the various disciplines together, so that we could be assured that the language used by various practitioners always meant the same thing.

None of this, of course, will ever happen. In a way, the very act of trying to "scientize" alternative therapies would rob them of their essence, and of their natural appeal. And natural appeal is something they seem to already have in spades. The earlier table may give some insight as to why. It may be true that much of what they treat is self-limiting illness anyway, but the same could be said of traditional medicine. In the end, what counts is what the consumers think, and whether they believe they are getting value for their money and their time. According to the *JAMA* survey, the amount of money spent on alternative therapies by Americans during 1997 was $27 billion—virtually identical to the amount spent on out-of-pocket expenses for all physician services. That tells us something about the value that consumers think they are getting from alternative medicine.

The comparable numbers for Canada are not available, but they must be similar. For one thing, Canadians do not pay for physicians' services out-of-pocket, a point which would skew the behaviour as well as the numbers. What is significant in Canada is that this segment of the health industry is the only one that cares what consumers think or want, and it is the only one that will respond to their expressed desires. Its growth in this country is therefore assured, and perhaps that growth will even bring about an evolution in the role it eventually plays in the larger health-care picture. All it takes is a glance at the table above to see that, unless traditional medicine has something more to offer than mere science, it doesn't stand a chance against the seductive powers of alternative medicine.

"Doc in a Box" Comes to Town

Without a doubt, the other raging success story in health care has been the proliferation of walk-in clinics, a service tailor-made to the needs of a public on the move with little time to waste. The phenomenon has been all the more impressive because it has occurred against powerful opposition.

One might well say that walk-in-clinics don't have a friend in town. They are despised by family physicians, who view them as opportunists taking the easy work and leaving the hard part for them. It should be no surprise, then, that they are also hated by the largely GP-influenced medical associations in control of the details of the provincial fee schedule which governs how much doctors are paid. Less obvious but no less powerful is the distrust of specialist physicians, who see walk-in clinic doctors as "fly-by-night" operators that they never meet, since they tend to move around more often and never do in-hospital work. Finally, they are hated by governments, who see them as money wasters generating profit by encouraging visits for minor ailments—exactly the opposite of the philosophy the governments are trying to promulgate. Yes, one could definitely say they don't have a friend in town. No one wants them, except the public.

And that has been enough to ensure not only their survival, but a phenomenal growth in market share. That market share consists not only of patients, but also of young physicians who opt for more simplicity in their careers, adequate time off, and a lucrative income for relatively stress-free work. Who can blame them?

Like them or hate them, it seems that walk-in-clinics are here to stay. But if you're not sure exactly what the term really means, you are not alone. A recent initiative by the BC Medical Association to make walk-in clinics "less economic" had a lot of difficulty agreeing on a definition that would not have affected at least some conventional family practices. It's not that they stay open late, and it's not that they encourage spontaneous visits without appointments. Regular doctors' offices often do the same. Walk-in clinics encourage people to visit for minor complaints, hoping to boost their income by boosting volume. The BC Medical Association finally decided to use this definition to amend the fee formula. The plan—called "Heavy Lips" because of the acronym HVLIPs—identified "high-volume, low-intensity practices" by their billing patterns, and dropped the fee schedule to 50 percent once the daily volume seen by any one doctor reached 45. The plan did not work, however, because doctors knew they could work to the maximum. When they reached that number of patients seen, they simply booked the rest of the day off.

But why does all this matter when walk-in clinics are clearly meeting a consumer need? While many people still carry in their minds the Marcus Welby-like image of a benevolent doctor, their behaviour works to erase that entity altogether and results in some surprises they had not bargained for.

For instance, a typical patient comes to Emergency with a urinary tract infection that has already been treated by a walk-in clinic doctor, but has become worse. The patient assumes the information about her illness is easily accessible to the doctor in emergency, but, of course, it is not. The clinic doctor may or may not have taken a culture, but which lab took it is unknown. Unless it is during daytime hours, it is impossible to locate the clinic doctor to ask, so the emergency physician repeats some of the tests and treats the patient with a wider spectrum antibiotic than necessary to cover all possibilities. The result? For the patient, over-treatment and loss of continuity, and perhaps an unnecessary yeast infection as a side effect of the broad-spectrum antibiotic. For the system itself, duplication of costs, and a loss of income for her GP—not significant in itself, perhaps, but highly significant in terms of the skewed incentives it creates, as we shall see later.

A second typical example is the patient who sees a walk-in clinic for control of hypertension, then ends up in Emergency and is admitted to hospital later when she has a stroke. The patient suddenly has no personal physician who knows her in the hospital, since the walk-in clinic doctors don't maintain hospital privileges. She may not have known it at the time, but the act of seeing someone out of convenience has bought her a lonely time without anyone with whom she has a relationship, at one of the most vulnerable times in her life. When asked why they didn't see their own physician for their everyday needs (if, indeed, they bothered to keep a physician of their own at all), many people say it was only a minor thing and they "didn't want to bother" their own doctor about it.

The same person who didn't want to bother her doctor with the "easy things" will probably see her own doctor for her depression the following year. She may choose to do so this time, or perhaps her walk-in clinic told her to do so because they don't want to get involved in complex things. Now, not only does her GP not know about the urinary infections, even worse, he (or she) resents getting paid the same money for a time-consuming and labour-intensive problem while the colleague in the walk-in clinic is still seeing minor ailments. What the GP certainly notices is the increased acuity of the office workload, now that the easy things are all going to walk-in clinics, and that will make the GP think more seriously about making life easier by giving up hospital privileges, too.

"If you can't beat 'em, join 'em," the saying goes, and that is exactly what many GPs are doing. If they don't move completely into a walk-in clinic situation, then they will at least give up the

most difficult and least lucrative part of their practice, which is the in-hospital work.

This may seem a far-fetched line of causal reasoning to some people—why should the fact that some patients sometimes use the convenience of a walk-in clinic instead of their doctor cause a flight of GPs from in-hospital work? The point is, it doesn't when it is occasional, but certainly does when the practice is widespread. It has now reached the point where doctors are resigning their hospital privileges *en masse* and retreating to their offices only—which is essentially what walk-in clinic work really is. It may not be as satisfying, but it pays the rent and is a lot less stressful.

So, now the casual visitor to the walk-in clinic has helped to create a system where not only does she not have her GP with her when she has to be admitted to hospital, nobody else does, either. And the large-scale loss of GPs from hospital practice means a breakup of patient care into little segments, each with a specialist, but with no one looking after the entire patient. It also means the GPs become increasingly less integrated and less relevant in treatment of serious illness, so that when they are suddenly called upon to deal with a medical crisis, they have lost their skills. All this from one measly decision to seek attention from a walk-in clinic because of a bladder infection. Who would have guessed it?

The answer is "no one," because no one is educating the public on these matters. The more shortsighted and unaware people become, and the more disenchanted GPs become with their work, the more this will happen. The more people move and become busy with their work, the more they will rely on walk-in clinics. The more GPs become financially hurt by being there for their patients in hospital, the fewer GPs there will be. And the fewer the GPs left, the harder it will be to find a GP willing to accept new patients, and the harder will be the work for the ones left still doing it.

In other words, we have started a self-feeding downward spiral. Walk-in clinics are a classic one-way phenomenon. They are not only here to stay, they are turning into a bigger and bigger component of our health-care system all the time.

Mrs. S. W. had been a spry 82-year-old, living on her own in a small apartment before she became ill. No one looked less at ease in an emergency department than she did, but her family had impressed her with the realization that she had no other alternative and brought her to the hospital. Her cancer had spread, presumably, and now she was too weak to manage at home. She was able to give only a sparse history.

"And when did you say this all started?" I pressed her again with the same line of questions. Her complaint of weakness and shortness of breath was so non-specific, it could have been caused by any one of at least a hundred different problems. Her son-in-law seemed impatient with the prolonged questioning and repeated his earlier suggestion, "Her doctor has all of her history. Why don't you check with him?"

I swallowed. The chances of finding her GP on a Sunday evening were remote enough. Worse still, I knew she had been managed by several specialists at one of the downtown hospitals, which meant that her family doctor might not have all the information I needed. "Which doctor do you usually see in the office?," I asked. The patient was unable to answer clearly, but again the son-in-law offered his advice.

"Dr. Keller is her own doctor, but she has a hard time getting to his office all the time, so she sometimes uses the walk-in clinic. You know, for small things."

That was not helpful. The walk-in clinic was closed, and it was impossible to find out when they had last seen her or what they had done.

"Why did you go to the hospital downtown?" I asked. "Don't you live nearby?" In fact I knew she lived three blocks from this Emergency department, but all of her records were in a different hospital at least 20 km away.

"My doctor sent me to a specialist downtown, and then they kept me there for tests. I had to see three different specialists there." She seemed almost proud of the attention she had received.

"And now that you are really sick, you've come back here to this hospital," I completed her thought for her.

"Yes. Well I only live down the street, dear." Her reply was straightforward and bore no insight whatever. She had allowed all of her care to be done at a faraway hospital and used walk-in clinics whenever convenient. Naturally, she assumed her records were available anywhere. It had never occurred to her that now, when she had become really ill, her actions had left her isolated without a physician who knew her.

Battle of the Bulge

The best-known demographic phenomenon of the 20th century is the baby-boomer generation, sometimes referred to as "the bulge" because of the resemblance to a large meal gradually passing through the length of a snake's body. The boomer generation has been followed by a succession of "Me" generations, pampered by the consumer society they live in and increasingly concerned with themselves. What these generations have in common is a set of experiences that give them, as consumers, an array of choices, and the freedom to determine the direction their own tastes will take. This stands in direct contrast to the socialist view of society, in which an elite few determine what is in the best interests of society and—through force or political power—impose their will on those they deem less able or willing to take control. It is a set-up for a conflict, as the two opposing forces collide, each trying to impose their own sense of order on how society works.

In the field of health care, the battle lines are clear. Will individuals be able to determine the course of their own care, or will the state succeed in imposing the greater good as determined by those holding political influence? The stakes are high. At the one extreme, we would have a consumer-driven system, free to evolve in the direction chosen by those able to pay. On the other, we would have a rigid structure in which waiting times reflect the fact that the providers and not the consumers are in control. We can watch the process in action as the debates about public-only vs. public-private health care unfold.

What is most significant in determining the future is the fact that the baby boomers have now entered their fifties and sixties—the very years in which their need for health care interventions will double or triple. It is one thing to debate academics, but quite another when one's own life or the life of a loved one is at stake. If population demographics have anything to do with the outcome, those who have a stake in the dominance of the public system will be left wondering where they went wrong. It is a "Berlin Wall" that Canada faces within its own politics, as well as in its health-care system.

Much of the current mood in health care is driven by a determination to control the 'abuses' of the system. It is an accepted axiom that people use the health-care system like a thing of convenience, unaware of the effort or cost. Small wonder that they are unaware of the cost, since they are told repeatedly that health care is "free," and since they never have to pay, there is no way to obtain the feedback.

It seems like a simple oversight. Even if the costs are picked up, surely some awareness of the costs are warranted? For example, if people knew that the doctors' fees almost doubled after midnight, wouldn't they make more of an effort to come in earlier, or perhaps wait until the morning? Is this merely an oversight on the part of government, or is there something to be gained by keeping the public in the dark? Some think that it is a deliberate withholding of information to increase the apparent power of politicians and keep the public more dependent. Perhaps things are not so Machiavellian, but the fact that governments continue, year after year, to pass up the opportunity to give the public feedback or educate them about costs cannot help but make us wonder.

Abuse, on the other hand, is a matter of perspective. Very few people seek medical help with malicious intent. Most are worried about something and have no means of making their own diagnosis. The high frequency of common-cold-related complaints is an often-quoted statistic that makes it seem like people have nothing better to do than visit doctors at the first sign of a runny nose. Looking behind the statistics can be most instructive.

First of all, we might ask how the statistics on "common cold" are gathered. In most cases, it is by analyzing the diagnostic codes that physicians mark on their electronic billings. Remember, though, that physicians must put a code in the claim in order to get paid, and none of the codes are checked. Many patients have more than one complaint, or have a string of related complaints, which do not lend themselves well to picking a single code. Doctors end up doing what most people would do under similar circumstances: they find the easiest path and follow it over and over. Instead of memorizing hundreds of diagnostic codes, they remember only a few, predominantly the ones they use most of the time. The real reason people come in with colds can vary, from concern about strep-throat, to sinus infection, to symptoms of fever that some people are concerned about. Some people come because their spouses finally pressure them into coming. Yet again, others don't know they have flu and complain of tiredness. The doctor notices an elevated temperature and diagnoses an upper respiratory illness. Instead of looking up the exact code, he enters the code for a common cold, since it is one he is familiar with. Anyway, no one checks.

No one does really check, but someone jumps to the conclusion that an awful lot of doctor's visits are for simple colds. If one forgets that a big part of any doctor's work is excluding serious diagnoses and simply reassuring people who couldn't possibly know what was wrong with them, then all of it can look a lot like abuse.

A prominent example is what happens during flu season. Visits to emergency obviously go up, but not because people come in with "the flu." Most people come in because they are worried about something. Either the fever is higher than they expect, or the cough is too persistent and they begin to worry about pneumonia. Many flu illnesses involve headache and fever, and people worry about meningitis. The fears are fanned by horror stories told by family or friends and by the inability of most non-medical people to be able to diagnose themselves. The doctor examines them, reassures them, and writes down a diagnostic code for a simple cold.

Those "Unnecessary" Visits to Emergency

Mr. G. W. had managed somehow to get overlooked while in the Emergency waiting room. That may sound difficult, considering that he was left in a wheelchair in the middle of the traffic area, where everyone had to step around him, but that was the way things went in a busy emergency department in the middle of flu season. Someone finally took pity on him after an hour or so in the wheelchair, and moved him into an examining room. I finally saw him there about an hour after he had arrived.

His first words were apologies for coming in. He didn't want to bother anyone. I could see from the chart that he was a 36-year-old lawyer, and not someone accustomed to complaining about trivial things. He was unshaven and had that grey-green skin colour of someone who was more than a little ill.

He described his symptoms of fever, diarrhoea, headache, vomiting and cough. "What time is it?" he asked. "My wife will be back in an hour to pick me up. She dropped me off at the door and gave me royal shit for wanting to come in just because of the flu. Honest doc, I feel really sick."

Indeed, he did look quite sick. A lot of people with the flu get quite dehydrated and sick, but perk up quickly once they receive some intravenous fluids. I decided to initiate that, along with my favourite drugs for nausea. I would run some blood work in the meantime and reassess him when he had been re-hydrated. A litre of fluid generally makes a big difference. The place was very busy, and I wanted to get away to see another patient, but felt I had better do a quick physical first. I raised the covers.

"What's this for?" I asked, pointing to a surgical scar on his upper abdomen.

"Oh that," he replied. "Nothing. I had my spleen out about five years ago after a car accident."

This changed the situation a great deal. A splenectomized patient has a compromised immune system and almost no defences against infection. A much higher degree of suspicion had to be used. I put my hand behind his head and gently lifted.

"Yow," he exclaimed as his neck stiffened against my movement. Suddenly my plan changed. He had classic signs of meningitis. Quickly, I called one of the nurses and explained. Blood cultures would be done immediately and a mega-dose of penicillin was being drawn up. Within a few minutes, I had finished a lumbar puncture (or spinal tap), and had the fluid to prove my diagnosis was correct. Luckily for him, his penicillin was administered quickly, before he began to deteriorate.

If he had listened to his wife and continued to assume he just had the flu, he would have died at home. Later I explained this, in the nicest tones I could muster, to his incredulous wife. "He's a lucky man," I offered, trying to be supportive.

Lucky he was not. In spite of receiving antibiotics quickly, he had almost no immune system and continued to worsen. Within a week, he had surgery to remove a portion of his brain that had become necrotic. Within another week he was dead, in spite of aggressive treatment and all the technology we had at our disposal.

Why do we expect people to know their diagnosis before they come to a doctor or emergency department?

One of the most difficult notions to fight is the conviction by many lay people and politicians that the trouble with our healthcare system is too many people coming to emergency. If somehow only those people who really needed emergency care came to hospital, then things would be much better. It is understandable that some people find the idea appealing and attractive in its simplicity. They could not be more wrong.

In a typical busy urban emergency department, about 20 percent of arriving patients need admission. These form the "verified truly ill," designated by the examining physician as needing overnight care after a diagnostic workup and often after a failure of a short course of treatment in Emergency. Another 20 percent are assigned one of the rare stretchers by the staff, but are able to go home after tests or treatment. All of these people, by definition, needed to come to an emergency department. Of the other 60 percent, about half have various illnesses that need treatment such as suturing and x-rays, or for minor fractures or infections. They also need an emergency department even though they are not, strictly speaking, terribly ill. Such procedures are much more cumbersome and slow to do outside of hospital, and the outcome is not always initially clear. The remaining 30 percent have a variety of minor ailments that have aroused concern or worry, but respond to simple tests or reassurance. About a third of these, or 10 percent of the total, could probably have gone somewhere else instead of an emergency department—but again, only half of these people are amenable to education and the other half, or about 5 percent, are chronically dependent or dysfunctional and will always depend on the emergency department for their care, because they tend to overreact as part of their natures.

In other words, the level of "true abuse" is probably less than 10 percent, and half of that is endemic to any emergency department and not amenable to treatment. So much for public education. Even assuming we could access all the other people and that they had a good idea what their diagnoses were (an unrealistic aim to begin with), the potential for decreasing workload is only about 5 percent, with an expensive price tag on the cost of trying to educate all the people that show up in Emergency. The real cost of that process would be measured not in dollars, but in lives.

Mr. R.S. was a 75-year-old man who finally came to emergency because he had a hard time breathing. He had never been sick a day in his life before this.

"When did you begin to feel like you couldn't breathe?" I asked.

"Oh, during the night it woke me up. I finally was able to get some sleep earlier, and then this breathing trouble woke me up."

"Were you having trouble sleeping before?" I asked, following up on his lead.

"Usually, I have no trouble, but this darn indigestion has been keeping me awake for a couple of days."

"Indigestion?" I asked. "Do you have that often?"

"No," he replied, "only in the last couple of days. It's been keeping me awake." He pointed to his mid-chest.

""Did you get this checked then, with your doctor or anything?" I asked, suspecting the answer.

"Oh no. I didn't want to bother anyone just because of some indigestion."

A quick EKG showed the truth. My thoughtful patient had kindly endured his heart attack at home for two days because he didn't want to bother anyone. Only when he began to go into heart failure from the damage to his heart muscle was he forced to come in.

The people most likely to respond to being told to stay out of emergency are not the perpetual abusers, but the conscientious people who are already more likely to wait too long before they seek help. As we increase the pressure on people to stay away from emergency, we convince a large number of people to volunteer their health and their lives.

People cannot be expected to know what is wrong with them before they come to Emergency. That is the job of the department, and almost all emergency departments are extremely quick at identifying the sick from the not-so-sick. That means that only a small fraction of time and resources are spent on those who are less sick. Forging ahead blindly with education campaigns to keep people out of emergency not only keeps sick people out—even if it succeeds, it cannot have an impact on the real need in emergency, the lack of inpatient beds.

A recent study of priority scores assigned by triage nurses in Emergency confirms this point. In most emergency departments, each patient is assigned a score from one to five, indicating the level of urgent need for care. The scores are assigned at the front door by an experienced emergency nurse, logged into a computer, and can later be compared to the probability of hospital admission. As expected, the rate of admission goes up as the priority scores go up, but the largest proportion of patients fall into the third level. A small but disturbingly constant five percent of patients eventually admitted were originally given priority scores of four or five by the triage nurse, indicating a low level of urgency—scores that usually mean the patient could have gone to a clinic or GP. These people, who in fact turned out to have serious disease (as indicated by admission to the hospital), had been mis-triaged by an experienced nurse at the door. How, then, could we expect a patient to diagnose himself, with much less knowledge than a nurse, and amidst all the personal anxiety? Expecting people to do this for themselves leads only to personal disaster. Yet, many in the public and many of our politicians continue to advocate this, and are even convinced that it is the way to save our system.

Some provinces have even sunk money into Internet-based or telephone-based advice from nurses to help people avoid Emergency. The initiatives, though well-intentioned, are misguided and can result in even more Emergency visits as the nurses discover the difficulty of telling what is really going on by telephone and patients become more alarmist than before.

The Headache of Chronic Care

If not by keeping people out of emergency, the other answer to save our system lies in increasing the number of chronic care beds so we can free up the acute hospital beds for acutely ill patients. Chronic care costs less than acute care, we are told, so the conversion will bring a payoff.

It would, that is, if chronic care did not cost anything. The last decade or so of health care maxims is that the total number of acute beds would be enough if they weren't filled with as many chronic patients. Increasing the pool of chronic care beds became the answer to the dilemma of not enough acute beds.

Without question, there are patients receiving chronic care while tying up acute beds, but the number varies from one hospital to another and from one community to the next. An attempt was made during the early '90s to measure this "problem" and track whether it was getting better or worse. What really happens is that patients—typically elderly but still living in their own home—become ill and end up in an acute hospital, recover from the acute illness, but remain too weak or otherwise incapacitated to manage at home alone. Usually, the family, if they live in the area at all, are tied up with their own work and children so that no one can stay home to look after Granny. Nor is it an easy request for someone without training to look after a person who may require assistance for even basic bodily functions 24 hours a day.

It seems like an easy problem to measure, but of course it isn't. The term "ALC" (for alternate level of care) was coined to describe those patients who fit the description (the actual phrase used may vary somewhat from province to province, but all are an improvement over the colloquial terms used, such as "bed blockers"). The point at which Granny passes from legitimate acute care to an ALC status has been the subject of much discussion, but we finally, in the year 2002, have a series of objective criteria that are more or less uniform, even if a little arbitrary.

The first problem was one of motivation. Why should Granny move from a place that feeds her, keeps her clean and bathed, and even helps her stay active, when the alternative is going back to a place that is insecure, where she must spend her own money on rent and food? Since health care is free and the transition between acute care and chronic care is a fuzzy one at best, these patients tended to drift into long-term residence, always needing just a few more days to get better. Some, of course, were never going to get better and would need permanent placement in nursing homes or other long-term care facilities. Canadians have always insisted on health care being free, but at what point does health care turn into simple room and board that all Canadians must pay for?

There was no easy answer. Many hospitals, during the '90s, saw a need to start charging something for those patients who clearly no longer needed the services of an acute hospital. The number of patients so charged has always been only a fraction of those who might have properly been required to pay, because of our need as Canadians to make absolutely sure that those who were sent a bill had no shred of reason to claim they still needed anything more than custodial care.

Even this was a struggle. Many provincial governments simply outlawed the practice of charging for anything ever, to avoid any small chance of accidentally charging someone who had not completely passed the threshold into ALC. Many resisted for a while, but eventually caved in because of the need for cash and the desperate need for beds for new patients. The results were interesting.

First of all, the resistance was surprisingly low. Some people objected, but the majority seemed to accept the need to pay for their normal living expenses themselves. For hospitals, it generated a significant source of new and badly needed income. The shift of people out of hospitals, however, did not happen—at least, not to a significant extent. Curiously, the new income also removed some motivation on the part of the hospitals to move these patients out, since that would have removed a source of revenue.

Adam Smith would surely have offered the suggestion that if the patients were being charged for their room and board, but were still not choosing to leave, they were not being charged enough. The rates should go up until the desired effects were achieved. Alas, in most provinces, the rates public facilities may charge are strictly regulated. Hospitals are simply not free to charge what they need to charge to encourage people to move. In most provinces, the rates have not changed in years and are substantially lower than what someone would pay for living space in a comparable facility.

Before anyone gets too riled up about charging poor elderly patients for health care, I should point out that we are not talking anymore about people who need health care. We are talking about people who have come through their medical illness and are now in need of only living arrangements—perhaps with some support, but living arrangements nonetheless—that all other Canadians must pay for out of their own pockets. It is also a myth that older people are necessarily poor. Statistics show the opposite: the wealthiest Canadians tend also to be the oldest ones.

Accepting for the moment, then, that people who have completed their illness phase of their hospital stay should move out and make that free bed available for the next person who needs it, what is wrong with this picture? There is one other more familiar scenario that has been extensively studied, and which causes a similar problem.

Even socialist-oriented groups now acknowledge that rent control is a destructive policy that in the long run hurts the very people it is supposed to benefit. Yet it was all the rage, in the '70s and early '80s, as a way of making housing affordable to the less fortunate in society. Until it became clear that those same policies that forced landlords to limit their rents gave a signal to those who might have built more housing units to do something else with their money. When it became clear that government would not be able to take over where private investors had fled, the number of housing units fell, precipitating an even worse shortage of housing and forcing the non-regulated housing market to lofty heights. The market had spoken, and virtually no one in Canada still believes that rent control is a solution to anything.

Anything, that is, except in health care, where a form of rent control still dominates the prices that can be charged in extended care facilities. The same devastating effects are experienced—limited availability, the chasing away of investment, and making government the lone supplier for an ever-more-needed commodity. In this case, the damage is not limited to those who need long-term care facilities. It also is a major cause of the crowding in emergency departments and the difficulty of getting acute hospital beds for those who need them. What damage could be prevented if only a little basic economics were applied!

THE POLITICIANS

Passive or Active Players?

I magine an industry that repeatedly chooses a chief executive who needs to know nothing about the business to get the job, and then receives complete financial control over an enterprise without any clear sense of product, price or value. Add to that the certainty of having that chief executive replaced after only a few years in office with a new person, just as naïve, just when some learning about the industry might have started to take place. And last, remember that the personal careers and ambitions of these people have nothing to do with the industry, but are built on whatever illusions they can create during their term of tenure. Bundle these conditions together and you might have some idea of why our health-care system is floundering.

There is an urban myth prevalent in our society that politicians in ministerial positions do not get involved in day-to-day decisions, that complex ministries such as health are run by professional management staff who are apolitical and know lots about the industry. It is an illusion that has been allowed to flourish, in order to preserve the image that politicians would prefer to have as benign masters. Nothing, in fact, could be farther from the truth.

Politicians, after all, must reserve for themselves the right to assign how much money goes into the system, and by inference, where that money largely goes. Management staff members are allowed to make decisions on their own that have no monetary and no political implications, but how much of health care falls into that category? We may fuss at the political tampering with something as important as health care, but the fact that it happens is perfectly understandable.

Turn the tables for a moment and think what it must feel like to walk into the job. Imagine the discipline it would take to stay out of decisions that have a (hopefully) positive impact on something as closely watched as health care. Think of how difficult it must be to pass over an opportunity to take public credit for a new hospital, or perhaps a new diagnostic facility. Considering that the process of political advancement requires the accumulation of "points" over one's career, what better vehicle for this than spending on the most humanitarian of causes, public health care? What matter if the money being spent belongs in trust to the very people upon whom it is being spent? What politician, no matter how well meaning, could afford to forgo the opportunity of posturing for a small bit of political gain, especially if he (or she) is convinced that it is well deserved?

The sad truth is that there is no better opportunity for politicians to gain public approval than by associating themselves with the positive aspects of free health care. And since there is no public accounting for the process of making political points, the way is open for anything from benign photo-ops to outright political rape. Examples of each possibility in the spectrum exist.

The Original Promise of Medicare

As originally formulated, medicare was an answer to a particular problem. That was simply the fact that many Canadians could not afford to pay for hospitalization. The cost of physician's visits were not so much of a problem, since typical charges were small and most physicians had a relationship with their patients that they took care to preserve, no matter what their patients could afford to pay. There was, therefore, no widespread difficulty finding a physician when one needed one. Fees were typically negotiated on the basis of what people could manage, and often fees were waived altogether. It was simply what had to be done if one were serious about being in a caring profession.

Hospital fees were another matter, because hospitalizations could quickly become very expensive. Remember that in those days, physicians were likely to work alone, or if a hospitalization was required, it was a simple admission to allow one or two doctors to do what they needed to do. Still, since the cost of hospitalization could become prohibitive, insurance was readily available for this. Those people who had no insurance were billed, but rarely pursued if their finances were not sufficient to make it worthwhile. A large number of people simply had their debts written off by the hospitals, and the expectation of those write-offs was included in the amount billed to insurance companies. What was the problem?

The main problem was the concern that some people might not even try to access the system for fear of being confronted by a bill they could not afford. The second problem was the worry by some people that those receiving pro bono care would feel badly, being thereby reminded that they were charity cases. The answer was to pay for everyone's care, so those unable to pay were no longer being singled out.

Whether this was worth the public expense of paying for everyone's care—even those who could afford it—is not the issue. Some feel strongly that it was worth the cost to preserve the dignity of those without adequate resources. Perhaps so. What is important is to understand that the problem being addressed was not a widespread inability to access health care.

Perhaps, if things had stopped there, we might still have a workable if expensive system. But once started, politicians could not resist the urge to give even more, and they began to play the role of *providers* of hospitals and equipment in addition to being simple underwriters of cost. This upped the stakes considerably, but reaped major benefits in political points, because politicians could now pose in front of actual things, such as hospital wings and CT scanners, in addition to having a passport-style photo in the news.

Once governments became providers, the move to take care of the things they had provided turned into a reality. Governments were no longer merely underwriters and providers; they had become managers, trying to optimize what they had brought into the world. It was about this time that the move to global budgets was being made. By deciding how much money each facility was granted, governments were making decisions that had an impact on actual patient care. This made the existing managers of hospitals merely agents of the provincial government.

Some of the most brazen examples of micromanagement by government were found in the forced mergers between hospitals during the 1980s and early '90s, such as occurred in the Toronto Hospitals, in the Vancouver General and UBC Hospitals, and at McMaster and Civic Hospitals in Hamilton, to mention only a few. Since the hospital managers were not in a position to argue with their political masters, they were forced to accept both their financial limits and their marching orders, and to do so quietly.

Faced with an escalating demand but a fixed amount of money

available through government, there were two options hospital managers could follow. The first was to work on efficiencies to increase their productivity within the fixed budget, and the second was to generate external revenue through extra billing.

The first of these has been a slow process, most of which has been to the benefit of the industry and to the Canadians who depend on it. The second provided an extraordinary opportunity for additional political gain for federal politicians. The Canada Health Act of 1982 was designed to demonstrate to the public that the federal Liberal Party was squarely dedicated to the principles of universal benefit for all by effectively banning all forms of extra billing by doctors or public institutions. At the same time that the law publicly proclaimed the duty of the provinces, it declined to declare its own obligation, which should have been to fix the federal contribution to cost. Instead, it left itself an option to unilaterally decrease the federal transfer payments to provinces actually paying for health care. The latter part was not perceived until much later, and even the extent of the reduction was not public knowledge until finally exposed by the provincial bodies themselves many years later.

Whether the idea for the Canada Health Act was an act of naïveté or a calculated, cynical move to secure the moral high ground for the Liberal Party at any cost is anyone's guess. Either way, it was highly effective at adding to the credentials of the federal Liberal Party and raised the stakes even higher in the race to show who was the ultimate guardian of the public good. Unfortunately, it also dashed any hope hospital managers might have secretly harboured of escaping from the funding straitjacket that all provincial health services were feeling at the time.

Secondary Agendas

As politicians found themselves increasingly in the driver's seat of health care, they gradually realized there was no reason to limit their gains to the original political points. They could also use the system to achieve other, ongoing political aims as well.

For example, the struggle against income disparity has been a major political theme in Canada for many decades. The whole system of transfer payments was set up to re-distribute wealth from the "have" to the "have-not" provinces. The income tax laws are another example of an action intended to correct, to some extent, the inequities of income, as different tax brackets acknowledge who has the ability to pay higher rates.

I profess no personal opinion on the merit of such policies and am merely pointing out that they are there. And, just as these policies carry out a political intent, so the same political intent has been seconded to the health-care industry. After all, if government is the master, then there is no reason not to be consistent and require health care to follow the same political direction as other government agencies.

Thus, provincial governments have not shied away from using their influence in health care to level out income disparities that existed between different social strata. One of the main targets has been the high income of doctors.

Various techniques have been used to limit doctors' incomes, including aggressive negotiations, restrictions on billing numbers, and publication of individual doctor's incomes. All provincial governments have participated in one or more of these tactics over the years.

The approach with doctors has been a contrast to the encouragement to unions representing other hospital workers, many of whom have secured generous remuneration packages giving them significant advantage over workers doing similar tasks in the private sector. Again, my intent is not to proclaim a moral position either way, but to simply point out that it has occurred and the difference in the way these groups are handled is part of the larger political direction all of our governments have taken to one extent or other.

The bias toward union workers extended not only to wages and contract benefits, but also to jobs themselves. When the BC government closed Shaughnessy Hospital in 1993, it guaranteed the jobs of all union employees who wanted to transfer to other hospitals, whether those hospitals needed them or not. No such provision was made for any of the physicians, who were left to find alternate employment any way they could. The opinion was widespread that the doctors could look after themselves, while the unionized staff could not. Whether one agrees with the sentiment is not the issue—my intent is to point out that the treatment was quite different, and that it was politically derived.

In 1999, the three BC unions involved in health care—representing nurses, technical staff, and hospital employee staff—published their position paper on the future direction of health care as they saw it. The paper, entitled "Blended Care," clearly outlined their position on a number of issues, including the role of doctors, whom they acknowledged were valuable but only when held within their narrow fields of expertise. They wanted the influence of doctors on health policy curtailed. In other words, they were proposing much more union content and fewer doctors on health advisory committees. The position was not new; what was new was that it was openly published and distributed.

This can be attributed, perhaps, to the fact that their proposal had become much more mainstream. They could well afford to do this, since the authors of the report were well represented on the advisory board used by the federal health minister at the time. They helped to form a major part of the Health Reform agenda that the federal health minister insisted the provinces accept before he was prepared to release additional federal funds. The back-and-forth of these negotiations occupied headlines during late 1999 and early 2000, prior to the federal-provincial agreement that preceded the federal election. Again, whether or not one feels doctors should be less represented is not the issue. What is impossible to miss is that once again, federal health dollars were being used to promote a political agenda other than the simple provision of medical care to Canadian citizens.

Public or Private?

Another example of ongoing political aims is the current controversy about public vs. private ownership of health care. It is well known that all physicians' offices are private operations but paid by public funds. The same is true for radiology services, most laboratory services, physiotherapists, and pharmacies. These are all privately owned and operated, providing a public service according to guidelines set by government, and paid according to the services they provide. Profit is the way every one of these services operates. Organizations that fail to make a profit after paying their expenses disappear very quickly from the landscape. And yet, public debate about public vs. private facilities ignores these widespread working examples of public-private co-operation, and portrays *ANY* non-public operations as a threat to the entire system of medicare.

Perhaps the press can be forgiven for being uninformed and responding to the hysteria, but the politicians deserve no such pardon. The fact is, as long as one side of the debate seems to be politically popular, many of our elected officials cannot resist the opportunity to milk the situation for personal political gain.

In the meantime, the political need to control costs has, to an increasing extent, driven public policy. It was the driver in the decision to decrease medical school enrollment, since the number of doctors working in the country seemed to be directly related to costs. No more sophisticated thinking than that was needed. It supported the capping of medical fees, popular in many provinces, and it supported what amounts to fee-capping of hospitals, in spite of the expanding amount of work they are continually being asked to do.

The political perspective also explains one aspect of the picture, which is why the hospitals are in the worst shape of all the pieces of the health-care puzzle. Doctors certainly feel they have suffered, and so they have, but for sheer endurance, the hospitals in our country win the prize. The reason for this is, while governments have repeatedly tightened the screws on both, the doctors at least have had—in their provincial medical associations—some degree of political protection, and have more than once gone on the offensive to offset the damage. Hospitals, of course, have been able to do no such thing. Without the ability to go public and fight politics with politics as the doctors have, the hospitals have remained defenceless, in line positions that remained completely subject to the whims of their political masters. The extent of the damage has been correspondingly higher.

Political Points and How They Work

One might be excused for thinking that political "points" are things that come around at semi-regular occasions when politicians get an opportunity to pose for media photos. The process is much more pervasive and insidious than that.

One major way in which political power can be perpetuated is through the withholding of information. In the case of medical care, politicians playing this game have an opportunity to profit from unpredictability in the system. An analogy can be found in the way some parents give—or withhold, at their discretion—an allowance to their children.

Imagine a family in which a parent provides a regular allowance, calculated to be adequate to the child's needs. It may, in fact, be adequate at the outset, but often falls short, especially as the child becomes older. The child becomes dependent on the allowance, and is therefore beholden to the parent, but at the same time is forced into the position of constantly begging for more. The parent, on the other hand, may realize that the allowance is barely adequate and occasionally gives a bonus of some sort, which temporarily appeases the child. What happens is that the parent is firmly in the position of power, holds all the money, and decides when and how much to give. He or she may rationalize the decisions to award a bonus as something reserved for rewarding good behaviour, such as mowing the lawn or cleaning a room. The child, in the meantime, becomes resentful, because he sees the bonus as an unpredictable event—one completely at the whim of the parent.

Politicians (and I say politicians, because the management staff in health care rarely have any real discretion with money) have the opportunity to play a similar game. They may, in fact, see the various sectors in health care much the way a parent sees a large number of children, always wanting more and rarely showing any gratitude for what they have already been given. In this case, the job of the parent becomes one of trying to play a middle road, showing as little favouritism as possible, but always needing to 'make up' for one relative deficiency or other. The origin of the process may have been the ability to extract political points when favours are granted, but in the end, it becomes a losing game for everyone. Eventually, both the parent and the children lose track of what the deal was, who owes what to whom, and all that remains is mutual resentment and mistrust.

Why aren't funding decisions made by formula instead? Adults don't live by the "allowance" model in their business affairs—why should health care?

The answer is that most provinces do, in fact, have formulas to govern where the money goes in health care, but the formulas are far from perfect and not generally made public. Making matters worse, the formulas are rarely allowed to operate as they were intended without political interference. This is because politicians don't like to give up decisions about budget increases to a formula, and will usually insist on being the final arbiter of where the money should go when the opportunity arises. Legitimately so, because they are accountable for the money being spent and feel obliged to make sure the 'buck' stops with themselves. The end result, however, is that the "allowance" method for health-care funding remains firmly in place in virtually all parts of Canada. No wonder so many health-care providers feel their ministries treat them like children.

The Power of Money

No one should underestimate the degree to which federal policies determine how much each province has to spend on health care. When medicare was originally conceived in Canada, the medicare Bill (C-227) of December 1966 proposed a so-called 50/50 formula by which the federal government would contribute 50 percent of the national average per capita cost for health care to the provinces, while the actual operation of the medical plans was left largely to the provinces. That simple percentage was changed to a more complex formula by the Established Programs Financing Act (EPF) in 1977, and the formula itself went through a series of changes during the 1980s, which effectively limited the EPF to two percent less than the growth in the GNP. In the meantime, the Canada Health Act, which was proclaimed in 1984, constrained the growing trend toward user fees by the provincial governments trying to balance their budgets and allowed federal funds to be withheld altogether if provinces failed to adhere to federal guidelines. The Act did not, however, provide a minimum federal contribution to the operation it pretended to support. Far from fixing the federal obligation to fund health care, federal transfer payments were further cut from 18.7 billion in 1994 to 12.5 billion by 1998—a drop of 33 percent in four years. The latter was on top of the lost ground and constraints that had been placed on provinces during the 1980s, all of it in a climate of at least four percent inflation and a falling Canadian dollar (most medical equipment comes from the U.S., and is therefore sensitive to the relative value of our dollar).

It is hard to come to any conclusion other than that the federal government has consistently raised public expectations of its health-care system and tried to hoard the political mileage that went with being the defender of medical care, at the same time as it shied away from its responsibility to pay its fair share. Anyone who follows current events in even a cursory way will recall the federal-provincial wrangling over the federal monies owed to health care that went on prior to the year 2000 federal election. The major result was the infusion within the 1999 Federal Budget of $11.5 billion into health care over the next five years. Although loudly trumpeted by the politicians as a renewal of the federal commitment to health care, what most people do not know is that the amount merely brought the federal contribution back to what its 1995 level would have been, without any adjustment for inflation or demographic change. Even that minimal redress was not immediately forthcoming, but is scheduled to be achieved over five years.

If that is not depressing enough, consider this. A province working on its budget for health care must face some stark realities that arise directly out of the way our tax system is structured. It is axiomatic that the shortages in nursing and other staff are resulting in major cost increases to provincial budgets, partly due to the amount of necessary overtime payments and to a loss of negotiating power in the face of staff shortages. As in any industry, salaries and staffing costs will consume the major portion of the budget. Let us say, as an example, that salary adjustments will create an additional expense of a billion dollars to a province's health care annual budget. Everyone knows that government is different from other payment agencies, because it can expect a significant portion of its salary expenditures back in the form of tax revenue. But only about one third of tax revenue comes back to the province while the rest, about 70 percent, goes directly into the federal coffers. In other words, assuming a differential income tax rate of 50 percent, a province that gives a billion-dollar raise to its health care workers can expect to receive only about 170 million back in provincial taxes. More significantly, it is also writing a cheque for about $350 million to the federal government.

Agents or Victims?

Politicians make easy targets, but one can hardly blame the early fathers of medicare for their intentions. After all, the financial model they decided to use was considered bold and progressive at the time, and was indeed used with apparent success in many other countries and in industries other than health. We have had, since those times, a few politicians who have abused their authority for political reasons. It is tempting to tar all of them with the same brush, but that would hardly be fair.

The majority of politicians are just people like the rest of us, perhaps with a more pressing desire to serve the public interest. Even those who are respectful of the sacred trust they have assumed are left with a serious problem. They have—especially those taking office in recent years—inherited a complex system with a momentum of its own, deeply imbedded in a prevailing paradigm that still enjoys a good deal of public support. At the same time as they are pledged to be prudent with public money, they hold the reins of a machine galloping away at increasing speed, all the while devouring the giant's share of provincial money. No easy fixes come to mind, and no one seems to have an effective solution to what seems like a black hole for government money.

In other words, politicians have become part of the cycle, like everyone else, and can be just as easily portrayed as victims of the catastrophe as its agents. Without any successful models to follow, it is unlikely that any politician would be able to discover a way out that would satisfy all the players. Unwittingly, some may make policies that further fuel the cycle and add to the woes of the system by damaging productivity and further increasing costs. The whole thing starts to feel, after a while, like simply a problem of money.

Clearly, there is a need for much more federal money than we have seen so far, even to restore the federal commitment to its historical levels, never mind make up for the added limitations imposed by the Canada Health Act. Is there a chance that any more will materialize?

The answer is yes, but not necessarily in a form that the provinces will appreciate. The agenda in Ottawa, as far as health is concerned, remains for now at least, firmly entrenched within the ideology pursued over the past decade as advocated by the Tommy Douglas Institute. We can expect a commitment to further downsizing the number of hospitals and doctors, while at the same time instituting "primary care reform" by expanding the role of community health clinics. In short, it is an acceleration of the same policy that has created havoc within the existing health-care systems across Canada.

It is no coincidence that the newly appointed head to the Canadian Institute of Health Research (CIHR), the major federal agency for funding health research in Canada was Morris Barer. It is also no surprise that Ken Fyke, who along with Bob Evans sat on the BC Health Commission in 1991, recently released his report on Canadian health care recommending more of the same medicine. Mr. Fyke has a long history in health care management and as deputy minister of health in Saskatchewan worked closely with Roy Romanow while he was premier of that province. The ring was completed when we heard that Mr. Romanow was chosen by the Prime Minister to conduct yet another inquiry into Canadian Health Care. In spite of all this, Canadians were willing to give Mr. Romanow the benefit of the doubt, while he consulted and considered for eighteen months. In the end, he failed even to acknowledge the damage being done by the *Dominant Model*, that his recommendations would further entrench. He would perpetuate a system, in which the services provided by hospitals have no value, and the interests of those who need these services are kept firmly where they are, at the bottom. As long as no market activity of any kind is permitted either public or private, no law and no amount of money will ever change that.

DIAGNOSIS AND PRESCRIPTION

Part Three

Making the Diagnosis

Where Do We Start?

Why is it that so many health care experts cannot agree on what is wrong with our system or what to do about it? Everyone seems to agree that major changes are necessary, but some people think the train is going in one direction, while others think it is headed in the opposite direction. It is easy to get agreement on change until we try to discuss exactly what those changes should be.

There have been several major attempts to look at the problems in our health care industry. Ten years ago, the Seaton Commission in British Columbia took on the mammoth task and issued their report. There have been many others. One major conference organized by Health and Welfare Canada, in 1997, concluded there was "enough money being spent on health care in Canada, but not in the right places." More spending was suggested on preventative measures, social projects, and community services. No one estimated the current and ongoing medical need and suggested we put a business plan forward to try to meet it.

It is an axiom in our country that there are no experts in health care, only proponents of one philosophy or another. Under these circumstances, it is impossible to sort out what is really going on without re-examining all of our assumptions. Just as it is impossible to settle a family feud by choosing one of the warring factions, so we need to go outside the industry and see how it would look to a non-Canadian, someone who has no vested interest in our internal affairs. The Canadian system of medicare was set up to look after the health needs of Canadians. Why isn't it working?

Lenin's Ghost

We began this book with a look at Eastern Europe and an economic system on the verge of collapse. A revolution founded on the principle of human equality ended up two generations later in the scrap yard of history, unable to fulfill its promises. Now, half a world away, we face a similar collapse at home within our health system, and a similar slate of broken promises. It would be foolish not to at least try to look for parallels.

The principles embodied in the Soviet idea of how economies are supposed to work should by now be familiar to us. The way to enforce equality is to abolish money as the way to exchange goods and services and replace it with a distribution plan determined by government. No longer will the market forces of demand be permitted to dictate supply. Instead, the state becomes the sole provider, replacing 'demand' with 'need,' which is for the state to determine, since it cannot be trusted to individuals.

Unfortunately, the forced breakup of the relationship between demand, supply, and price also disrupts the feedback mechanisms that steer normal economies. Gone is the role of money as an incentive for innovation and a feedback on productivity. Absent is the information consumer choices provide that might suggest future direction. And nowhere to be seen is the competition that keeps costs down and ensures that someone cares about what normal people want.

This is what I call the "*Dominant Model*" that has driven our health-care system for the past thirty years. It is an economic model with the sophistication of a giant soup kitchen, with one group of people deciding what will be in the soup and how much to give, and another group in the line-up waiting for their turn. It is a set-up for the scenario in which Dickens' character Oliver Twist implores his master, "Please Sir, I want some more?"

Poor Oliver had no chance. Even had his request been granted, he would have remained trapped in a subservient role, continually begging. That is because once inside this scenario, there is no escape. The answer is not to ask more of the kitchen, but to recognize the entire model is unworkable. Human beings have a right to make their own choices. The role of government is to represent their collective interests and protect them from unforeseen disaster, not to impose an ideology of how economies should work.

It should be clear by now that adding more layers to our current health system will not help, just as adding more cooks would not help change the dependency on the soup kitchen. Recognizing this central theme and how each individual element either supports or reverses the status quo of the *Dominant Model* remains the key to fundamental change. With a little bit of practice, one can begin to recognize which plans are simply embellishments to the soup kitchen and which represent true change. The major themes are simple: the role of money, the power of consumer choice, and the politics of those who want to keep their current jobs in the kitchen.

MONEY AND HOW NOT TO USE IT

Money was not originally a creation of government. It evolved as a way of exchanging goods and services, and when governments became involved, it was simply to stabilize the value of the currency as a medium for exchange. The Soviets changed all that and elevated money to an instrument of state authority, much like a system of tokens. The idea remains alive and well in Canada's medicare system today.

Think about it. The combination of fixed budgets for hospitals and a restriction by law on their ability to accept any other source of payment for their services ensures that nothing like an exchange takes place. It also ensures that no values can be assigned to hospital services outside of those determined by government.

The result is that global (i.e., fixed) budgeting has created a financial nightmare in the hospital side of the acute care industry. With no ability to adjust money to workload, reward productivity, or provide financial feedback to managers, we have brought the most destructive aspects of Lenin's experiment home to bed with us. After 30 years, we have succeeded in losing track of what anything really costs, and have made the knowledge we need to retrieve that lost information forever unavailable. The imperative of "ignore the market" has assumed a moral value in our society rivaled only by actual sainthood, and in this objective, Canadian medicare has been successful beyond our wildest dreams. Unfortunately, in this case, "the market" consists of sick people expecting reasonable care. The dream has turned into a nightmare, and Canadian hospitals all understand how Oliver must have felt.

THE LOWLY CONSUMER

> *Twice now I've been scheduled for surgery at your hospital to repair my left ureter in an attempt to save my left kidney. The surgery was cancelled on Oct. 10th, and again on Nov. 14th as no beds were available due to Emergency admissions filling the beds. This has had a huge impact on me and my family. Physically, I've deteriorated during the delays, leading*

to decreased physical activity, and I suspect it will continue to worsen if the delay continues.

The emotional impact has been devastating for me. It is extremely hard mentally to prepare oneself for surgery, only to have it cancelled the day/evening prior to the surgery. It has affected my day-to-day living and has had an impact on my husband and daughter. It is becoming increasingly difficult to maintain a positive mental attitude.

The financial impact is significant, as I am the main wage earner for my family. I will run out of sick time on Nov. 17th. I will then be eligible for Employment Insurance sick benefits that certainly won't pay all the bills.

I find these delays a tremendous hardship. I would like a response of what is being done to solve the problem of my delayed surgery. Please do not tell me, "We'll look into it." I would like to know what specifically is being done to solve the problem.

We have already seen the powerlessness of the consumer, in an earlier chapter, and this complainant is only one of many. She will eventually get her surgery, and then, if she is like most Canadians, will stop asking the hard questions. This is good, because the real answer is not what she wants to hear. A truthful administrator would tell her, "Get used to it." People who lived in the Soviet countries before 1990 would tell stories of routine five-year waits to receive a new car they had ordered, even if they had already paid for it. Apartments often required 15- or 20-year waits unless one had personal connections. Landline telephones (before the days of cellular) took between two and six years waiting. The people in these countries got used to it because, like our complainant, there was simply nothing else they could do. Our complainant's case is no different. Without some financial consequences to someone for failing to meet her expectations, she might as well understand that her power to influence change is simply not there. The consumer's place in medicare, at least as far as hospital care is concerned, is firmly at the bottom.

KEEPING THAT JOB IN THE KITCHEN

The third piece in the triangle is the resistance to change presented by the groups that currently benefit from the status quo. One might include the entire list, from nurses and doctors, to managers and lesser-skilled labour. Some are less easily replaceable than others, and have little real reason to worry. But worry they do, both individually and collectively.

Just human nature, we might say, and so it is. Nevertheless, the rigidity imposed by our collective systems for compensating labour of all kinds has played a big part in creating the shortages of needed staff that now plague us.

It is a scenario we have visited before. Every three years or so, two groups of people sit opposite each other at a table and argue over pay and issues of control in the workplace. The end result is an excellent test of debating skill and political power. Unfortunately, it has very little to do with supply and demand. Even if market forces are represented at the negotiating table, there is no ability to track changes before the term of the next contract. Furthermore, even a small underestimate in one agreement becomes multiplied in the next, because raises are traditionally viewed as increases over the previous rates rather than as independent events related solely to current market conditions.

Aggravating the lack of market responsiveness of the collective bargaining process itself, restrictions in workplace mobility complicate a bad situation and make it even worse. For example, a hospital may have an adequate number of nurses overall, but if there is a shortage of nurses capable of working in the operating room, and if the contract puts restrictions on the ability to move nurses into that position, a de facto shortage crisis has been created.

WHY DON'T WE CHANGE?

Change is always difficult, even in the best of times. But in addition to the usual problems of change, Canadian medicare faces two other barriers of daunting magnitude.

1. It is now 30 years or so, that Canadians have been following these policies in one form or another. Thirty years is a whole generation, which means we have very few managers remaining in the industry who have any recollection or any experience in working with anything different. Where will the ideas come from to move the control of our health care resources away from the managers and back to the consumers who need them?

2. As if that weren't problem enough, our politicians have saddled us with one more final disservice, by allowing the controversy to degenerate into a polarized "two-tiered" debate. As if the only alternative to the status quo is an American-style system! As if, even in the U.S., there were only one system instead of many different co-existing systems, as anyone who bothers to look would know. And, as if there were no other countries in the world besides the U.S. and Canada experimenting with ways of providing compassionate medical care.

I can excuse the public for succumbing to the fear tactics of the debate, and I can excuse the media for being ill-informed or even opportunistic, since that's the way they must make their living. It is harder to excuse the federal politicians who have taken a vow to serve the public interest, and who should know better.

Famous False Starts of the Past

Before we look at the prescription for change that I will suggest, it would be useful to examine some of the false diagnoses and failed cures of the past. None of them, as we will see, addressed the fundamental assumptions built into the *Dominant Model*. Perhaps this had something to do with why they failed. Some of these have already been touched upon in previous chapters, but they bear repetition, because by taking note of them we can hopefully avoid repeating our mistakes.

1. A PUBLIC SYSTEM IS LESS EXPENSIVE THAN A PRIVATE ONE:

Aside from the moral arguments supporting public medicine over the private, profit-oriented kind, there is a powerful and widespread contention that public medicine is inherently less expensive. The argument goes something as follows:

> *Private medicine is steered by the desire for profit, rather than the desire to help people, resulting in misdirected investment. For example, clinics performing cosmetic surgery, which can generate huge profits, will be favoured over those providing care for the mentally ill or those suffering from cancer, which are costly but fulfill a greater need in society.*
>
> *Public medicine is also cheaper because it is able to bring a sufficient organizational size to bear, resulting in a more powerful negotiating position with suppliers. It can also, as a government agency, be exempt from the requirement to pay taxes.*

These are very logical statements with a strong natural appeal. It is difficult, in fact, to find a problem with either of them. They both appear to be manifestly true.

The problem, however, is precisely that they are true, but only in the short term. The reason this is a problem is that it makes the logic seductive and the payoff real but short-lived. In fact, the move to public medicine did net us all a significant gain, which we realized at the beginning of medicare. The problem is that it was a one-time saving. The statements that claim public health care is less expensive neglect what happens over longer period of time.

They also assume that profit is there for the taking and neglect to look at the other side of profit—something that can occur in any private venture, and that something is called *loss*. Profit, when it does occur, is not simply there for the taking, but only comes as a *reward* for providing, in an efficient way, something that is satisfactory to the consumer. Private operations get a profit only if and when they are successful; otherwise, they get a loss. By contrast, in a public enterprise, everyone gets a reward whether successful or not.

And therein lies the problem with public economies. If everyone gets rewarded, there is no evolution toward excellence, and the trend for succession sinks firmly in the direction of mediocrity. None of that is apparent when the system is new and just at the starting line. Thirty years later, we all scratch our heads wondering how we got there and refuse to acknowledge the part we all played in the obvious.

2. THE PUBLIC NEEDS TO BE BETTER EDUCATED

It is hard for anyone to be opposed to education. However, relying on public education as a process to fix something that is outside its reach can be a dangerous tactic.

An example is the problem of crowded emergency departments. It is a natural reaction, after noticing that only 18 percent of patients who attend a busy ER get admitted to hospital, to wonder why the others are there. A listing of discharge diagnoses will reveal that a considerable number of people did not need to be in an acute care setting. Depending on how the statistics are done, up to 30 percent or more could have been managed in a clinic or in their doctor's office. How natural then, for the well-intended but uninformed critic to suggest that therein lies a problem, and that if we could educate even some of those people to go elsewhere, we could decongest the department for those with more serious illnesses. Even better, if 30 percent of people who visit their doctor's offices do so for simple colds that require no treatment, we could save a lot of money by teaching these people how to look after themselves and not bother a doctor at all.

Back to the ER. We know patients cannot command the treatments they want, since the physician controls treatment. People don't simply ask to be treated for a heart attack. They might try, but only if the doctor thinks it's a heart attack is treatment given. We also know that the cause of the crowding, in virtually every ER, is not the new patients coming in the door, but the patients who have already been seen, diagnosed, and admitted, and have no physical bed to go to within the hospital itself. These patients are forced to stay extended periods of time occupying their emergency stretcher and making it unavailable for someone else. Since patients do not get stretchers unless the nurse or doctor feels they need one, this also is not a resource affected by walk-in patients with mild ailments. Similarly for other resources in the department. Staff quickly identifies patients who require minimal effort, because that is what the department is for and what it does best. The most significant shortage in any ER is the shortage of stretchers because of admitted patients in the department. Most ERs can handle large numbers of patients with minor ailments who do not require stretchers. The ER crisis is not really an ER crisis at all—it is a hospital inpatient bed crisis, and when it invades the ER, it turns into an ER stretcher crisis.

In a typical busy emergency department, 40 percent of the incoming patients will be assigned a stretcher by staff because they seem legitimately ill and need care or investigation, and the others will be directed to a fast-track area. Of the fast-track patients, half will have legitimate minor problems, such as ankle fractures and lacerations, handled better in an ER than in an office. Of the remaining 30 percent, at least half will have a mixture of symptoms that need to be sorted out, like colds, pneumonia, and appendicitis.

That leaves only 15 percent for things that could really have been seen in a physician's office. Of these, at least two thirds will have reasons for coming to the ER, such as inability to get a doctor's appointment, or they are transient with no permanent physician, or they simply became frightened by symptoms they could not understand and could think of no other option than coming to the ER. Perhaps their symptoms came on at two o'clock in the morning. In a practical sense, no amount of education would have made a difference to these patients in terms of where they went for care. That still leaves about five percent who could have gone somewhere else if they had known better. Unfortunately, these are usually the ones most resistant to public education, and the least inclined to follow guidance when others offer it.

Even if they were, one has to question the wisdom of spending all that time and money on education when, at best, only five percent of the volume would be affected, especially when these are not the ones occupying precious stretchers.

So, let's get off the bandwagon that thinks public education is an answer for congestion in the ER. What about doctors' visits in general?

Sometimes we give more credit to people than we should. As we saw in an earlier chapter, an audit of assessments by an ER triage nurse at the time patients present shows the nurse's estimate of the 'severity' of the patient's condition. In most hospital ERs, these assessments are coded and recorded in a computer as part of the patient's chart. Let us remember that these are experienced ER nurses making assessments. It would be fair to say that any education system that brought patients' understanding up to the level of an experienced triage nurse would be successful beyond its wildest dreams. In other words, the nurse's triage assessment could be seen as a "gold standard" of the most medical knowledge that one could reasonably expect of any normal patient.

The first thing to notice is that assessments vary considerably from one nurse to another. Although most of the extreme cases, such as "most urgent" and "least urgent" do agree, there is poor agreement in the middle range of illness severity. The other thing to notice is that, while urgency levels do correlate with the chance of hospital admission as one would expect, there is a small but predictable number of patients given a low assessment by the triage nurse, then subsequently admitted for serious illness after the doctor's assessment and investigation. Several research studies have shown this to be a widespread phenomenon. Even under the best possible circumstances as achieved by an ER nurse, about five percent of patients with serious illness would be missed if they hadn't gone through the full medical examination.

But patients are not triage nurses. Not only do they lack the education and experience, they are subject to overwhelming pressures of family and are inside their own disease process, which destroys any hope of objectivity. This is why physicians are always advised never to try to treat themselves or their own families. So, the level at which a triage nurse operates is unreachable by any educational process—not only because of the information needed, but because it is not realistic to ever expect people to be objective about their own illness. And public education campaigns are costly and slow. That doesn't mean there are not identifiable groups (such as new mothers, heart patients, etc.) that it makes sense to target for education. What it does mean is that no one should pin their hopes on a general education system helping to reduce the current health care crisis.

It was wonderful, really. You hear so much about how awful it is in hospitals these days. I was really worried about coming in for this surgery. Makes you expect the worst, you know. But they couldn't have been nicer to me. Everyone smiled and was so pleasant to me. Those nurses sure earn their pay. They work so hard, and then they still have to be nice to people. This is a real nice hospital. The surgery hurt, of course, and that catheter is certainly unpleasant. Doctor says these bladder problems are just things that women get when they get older. Kind of what happens from childbirth. Now it isn't so bad anymore. It was sure nice to get that tube taken out and start eating real food again.

• • • •

It was awful, really. None of the nurses here seem to know what peri-care is. Have people stopped learning the basics of nursing care? Here I am, a week after my bladder surgery, and no one has even cleaned my incision. I had to wash myself. And I had to sit here and have five different nurses each take my nursing history, and each one wrote it out by hand in one of those books. Like who is ever going to read them? And why do it five times? Even when I pointed out that I had been over this already with one of the other nurses—even when I stressed what my problem was after my last surgery—I had to explain it all over each time. And if one more nurse comes in to take my pedal pulses just one more time, I'm going to scream. I've just had bladder surgery. There's nothing wrong with my feet. But I know if I make too much of a fuss, I risk getting punished. If they want to punish you, they just ignore you. Maybe it wouldn't have made a difference anyway. The last time I asked for my painkiller, it took them two hours to get it. Too busy, they told me. Couldn't interrupt the report during shift change.

Or change my catheter bag. Good thing I happen to be a nurse myself, otherwise how would I have known what to do? Can you believe it? Some people think they are getting good care here, just because people smile and talk nicely. I'm lucky. I know how to make sure I get what I need. But what about that poor lady over there? She just smiles and thinks everything is OK.

It also has one more meaning that many health planners have not thought of. If education means brainwashing people into doing what they are told, that is one thing. On the other hand, if it means true education, then it is unlikely that a well-educated public will accept some of the shoddy services that pass for health care in our public system. Education is a two-edged sword. It could also create a public that knows what it wants, recognizes the shortcomings of the current provider-centred system, and is prepared to demand something better.

3. TOO MUCH SICK CARE, NOT ENOUGH PREVENTION

Those who favour this view have suggested our system is driven by people with a vested interest in curing existing disease instead of preventing it in the first place. The model describes a greed-driven industry in which doctors unwittingly follow the "illness first, then cure" algorithm they learned in medical school. Medicine has, it can be said, originated in this paradigm, and has had trouble changing. At the same time, everyone knows what an ounce of prevention is worth. A system that neglects prevention is, therefore, destined for ultimate failure and financial ruin—which, as the song goes, is precisely what is happening.

Cogito ergo sum. The solution is to divert the resources currently going to feed the fire of the illness-oriented model and start to prevent disease instead. It is an idea with unassailable logic and a natural appeal of its own. Let's look at some of the facts it neglects to mention.

Smoking is an excellent example of a correctable behaviour that causes untold loss of life and disability. It was first identified as a link to lung cancer in the early 1950s, in a study published by the *British Medical Journal* that followed a cohort of British physicians who smoked. It is now almost 50 years later, and the notion that lung cancer could be prevented if people stopped smoking has

finally come through the science of demanding consistent reproducible results, the natural resistance of the public, and the legal
challenges by vested interest groups. The incidence of smoking is
finally showing a steady decrease, but not in all groups or in all
regions. Worldwide dependence on smoking is yet another
problem, with Canada perhaps leading the way in reform, but
making only a small dent in the profits being made by the world
tobacco industry. Even in Canada, with decreasing smoking rates,
we know that it takes 20 years to form lung cancer, so it takes 20
years after people quit the habit before we see a decrease in the incidence of new lung cancers.

The bottom line is that this is a hard ship to turn around, with
a substantial lag time between when the investment is made and
when the payoff, in terms of decreased disease, occurs. True, not all
diseases have such a long timeline or such a resistant natural history, but many have even longer ones. The diseases associated with
alcohol, family violence, and behavioural disorders come to mind
as ones particularly resistant to change.

Not that we shouldn't be trying. What it does mean is that the
timeline for significant reduction in disease is a long one, and
should be pursued *at the same time, not instead of* the treatment of
existing illness. Too often, the argument has resulted in a re-direc-
tion of funds by politicians eager for an answer that doesn't cost
more money, creating an even worse problem in the treatment side
of health care.

And speaking of money, the age-old proverb describing the relative values of prevention and cure may not stand up to close
scrutiny after all. In the case of smoking and lung cancer, for
example, at the same time as we save people from the scourges of
lung cancer, we create a cadre of elderly people who are succumbing to other illnesses such as stroke, diabetes and heart disease, all with their attendant costs. Before we go on a spending

spree with the money supposedly saved by disease prevention, it would be smart to wait until all the accounts are in.

Unfortunately, what has happened is that the vociferous arguments in favour of illness-prevention instead of illness-cure have made the situation actually worse instead of better, by creating a group of people with a feeling of moral conviction often not accessible to simple facts. At the same time, they have succeeded in diverting funds into unproven schemes that claim merit merely on the basis of their objective rather than on demonstrated success. Lifestyle medicine, health foods, and megavitamin therapy come to mind, but there are many others. All of this is done at the expense of essential treatment for those who are in need today. In the meantime, the backlog of need has increased and the gap between what we can provide and what we can afford has widened.

So much for this wrong diagnosis. Now, let's look at another one.

4. TIGHTENING THE BUDGET
(AND WHY IT ALWAYS ENDS UP COSTING MORE)

J.H. is a 67-year-old man who phoned and left a message with the hospital's administration to complain that his surgery had been cancelled. As the medical administrator on duty that day, it was my job to return his call and deal with the complaint. Before doing so, I looked up his file, and saw that he had been scheduled for a partial lobectomy, a removal of part of the lung after having recently been diagnosed with lung cancer. The date was March 2 and the surgery had been booked on January 5—a wait of only eight weeks. Not unusual in our facility, but well beyond the four-week guideline for cancer surgery. It had been a bad week, with the Emergency department overflowing, two patients who should have been in the ICU staying two days in the post-operative recovery area, and the rest of the hospital in crisis. Seven other surgeries had also been cancelled that week. I decided to call him and beg that he understand our situation.

Before doing so I decided to read the rest of his file. The surgery had been booked in January, but that was after his bronchoscopy had been completed on January 2, showing malignant cells. The first evidence that anything was wrong was actually on October 12 when a plain chest x-ray ordered by his GP was typical for lung cancer. This prompted the necessary referral to a specialist, which took four weeks, and then a CT scan of his chest (which could only be ordered by a specialist), which was required to better define the lesion seen on the plain chest X-ray. The CT scan, done December 10, confirmed invasive cancer. The next step was a cardiac check-up with an echocardiogram, a mediastinoscopy and bronchoscopy, which were both done as soon as possible after the Xmas holiday. It would not have been appropriate to book the surgery before these tests were complete. But his total wait was clearly much longer than the eight weeks showing on my computer screen.

I phoned him back with more empathy than I might otherwise have had. "Yes," I said. "I realize you've now been almost five months since your diagnosis. I will do what I can to have your surgery re-scheduled soon." After I hung up, I made sure his surgery was re-booked later that same week.

I knew quite a bit more than I had let on while on the phone. I knew that our statistics would show a wait of only eight weeks for his surgery, when in fact the true wait had been more than 20 weeks. I also knew that all of his tests could have been done in two days had he been admitted to the hospital for them, as was once the practice. It had been at least ten years since we stopped admitting people for tests that could be done as an outpatient, as a way of saving beds and money. The last thing that I knew was that his CT scan four months

earlier had showed an invasive cancer that might have bene-
fited from surgery at that time. Any opportunity for cure had
long since passed. Had we known it would take so long to have
his surgery booked, it would have made more sense to save the
money and not do any tests or surgery at all. We could have
simply recommended palliative care instead, got the same
results, saved us some money, him an operation, and not raised
any false expectations for a cure.

It was too late. Telling him his surgery was a waste of
time now would be a cruel blow, even though that was the
truth. Putting him through an operation for nothing seemed
equally bad. The wait had not saved any money, and had
wasted a perfectly good operation. Even though the case was
typical of a widespread problem, it was one that could never
show up on any public audits, either inside or outside the hos-
pital. Who were we still trying to fool?

The most natural reaction to runaway costs is to restrict budgets across the board. The fact that this is tried on almost an annual
basis and ends up raising costs instead of lowering them is taken
only to prove that what is needed is more resolve and a willingness
to 'stick to one's guns.' Uncontrolled spending certainly seems like
the biggest threat to health care, and is certainly the biggest menace
to fiscal accountability.

Understanding why simply cutting back does not work and
how the process ends up actually increasing costs is easier if one
understands how the Principle of Sub-Optimization works. All
large systems are composed of smaller units or departments, each
with their own managers and their own budgets. Across the board,
budget cuts are aimed at decreasing costs without changing the
overall aims of the organization. Instead, each sub-unit receives a
cut in budget, often carefully balanced in an attempt to be 'fair'. In

fact, the preoccupation with fairness is a good tip-off that trouble is lurking around the corner.

Take, for example, an industry like a grocery store that is having financial trouble and decides to cut back on its payroll by cutting all department budgets by 10 percent. Now the truck drivers deliver their full loads less frequently and leave the unpacking for the clerks. But the clerks also have staff cuts and are unable to stock all the shelves, leaving the helper staff to spend more time searching for items that customers ask for. A cut in the computer department leaves the smaller staff of cashiers with an older inventory system which holds up customers, causing longer line-ups, and creates more work for the stocking clerks. And so it goes. In the end, things cost more because each department has off-loaded to its neighbours, and the added inefficiency created by the disruption threatens to cripple the organization, creating more costs of its own.

The components of our health-care system also depend intricately on each other. For example, the radiology unit must meet its trimmed budget and does this by decreasing the number of CT scans that are done. This creates a backup of patients on the wards who are now consuming more nursing time waiting for CT scans. The nursing units meet their altered budget by cutting staff, which causes an increase in patients waiting for admission in the emergency room. The excess workload in Emergency faces its own budget restrictions, of course, and forces ambulance attendants to put in overtime while their patients are waiting for stretchers in the crowded emergency department. One hospital meets its budgetary restrictions by decreasing elective admissions, forcing them to go to the next facility or to an endless stream of different doctors' offices, trying to find one that can help.

Please, doctor. Don't send my wife home again. We've been here four times already. Twice last week, and then we went to one of the downtown hospitals, because her doctor practices over there. He thought it might be easier to get her admitted there. They kept her in overnight on morphine, but then sent her home in the morning. She's been in pain since then and hasn't slept for two nights. She had an ultrasound done here last week and she was told she had gallstones. They told us we would have to find a surgeon somehow, but then they just sent her home. How are we supposed to find a surgeon when we get sent home?

Please doctor. Wouldn't it just be easier to do the surgery and get it over with? We both know she has to have it done. It's filled with stones on the ultrasound. You can look at the report yourself. It was done here last week. I know the emergency department is full, but we can't go anywhere. Can't you see she's been crying all night? Don't send us home again. We're so sorry to be a bother to you, but my wife just can't go home again.

And so it goes. Each sub-unit meets its tightened budget by off-loading work onto another sub-unit. Each meets its raised workload by working harder and faster, and by taking more short-cuts and risks. Eventually, new departments have to be created to keep the newly created problems under control. As things get more complex, all of these become essential pins that hold up the structure—without them, things seem like they would collapse. And all the while, the total cost keeps climbing.

But things do not completely collapse, not as long as the staff remains available and are willing to compensate. Instead, cost continues to rise, driven by those situations in which patients' demands simply cannot be ignored, such as emergencies. The critical point, where costs begin to rise exponentially, occurs when staffing shortages become so severe and so commonplace that they consume almost all the administrator's time and burn up money in overtime rates. The damage is costly but still reparable until the time when the 'increased resolve' turns into a complete unwilling-ness to accept feedback, and staff begin to desert their jobs because of burn-out. A trickle of resignations can quickly turn into a tor-rent as the workload on those that remain is made even worse. That is the point at which the flight of valuable staff permanently destroys infrastructure. The cost of repair, even if possible, is many times the amount saved and would take decades.

Tracy sighed as she hung up the phone. There was simply no one to come in to cover the night shift this time. This had never happened before. Sure, people were burnt out and they complained a lot, but when things got desperate, they always pitched in and somehow the department got through. True, the mood had been different over the last few months. Everyone kept saying it had never been this bad before. The demand for overtime and the pressure under which people worked were more than any emergency department should have to accept. And yet people continued on. It seemed like just all talk, this gloom and doom. Tracy sighed again. An ambulance had just pulled up outside the door, with its red lights still flashing silently. A small throng of apparently des-perate people was waiting patiently at the triage desk, trusting the big red sign outside the door that said "Emergency Depart-ment." One was holding a bloodied towel, while another held a basin for her child who was retching quietly.

There was no doctor this time, and she was the only nurse. Everyone knew there was a limit to how much people could compensate for and the pressure the staff had to work under. Still, there was always the illusion that things could continue as always in spite of it all. After working her fifth 12-hour shift in a row, Tracy wondered what would happen

*if she simply walked out the back door. Maybe it was bound
to occur someday, like people said. But why could it not have
happened on someone else's shift?*

The simple lesson of sub-optimization is taught in all basic business courses. It explains why arbitrary budget cuts in the absence of a change in corporate direction destroy efficiency and therefore result in an increase, not a decrease, in overall cost. And yet, we seem doomed to repeat the exercise every few years in health care. The only way to achieve true cost savings is to make the hard decisions and choose which of the things we do can be discontinued altogether. Why are we unable to learn from our own experiences?

5. WE SPEND TOO MUCH ON END-OF-LIFE CARE:

This is a compelling statement, easily backed up with statistics. Depending on the way we look at it, up to a quarter of the money spent on health care is spent during the last month of life. It is hard to avoid the implication that we are wasting money by over-responding to terminal events, and that if we redistributed some of that spending early on when it made more of a difference, we would all be better off. Is it really true?

*Mr. H.B. had become a distressing case. Hospitals are
accustomed to people dying, especially at the age of 79, but not
when they had walked into the emergency ward on their own,
talking normally. Now he was unconscious and on a venti-
lator in the resuscitation area of Emergency, paralysed from a
broken neck.*

*It was one of those rare series of events that make everyone
wonder what could have been done differently. A car accident
the day before had apparently resulted in a minor neck injury
with a negative X-ray done in a different emergency ward.
When he returned to Emergency because of persistent neck*

pain, a repeat X-ray that was also normal did not seem enough. Somehow during the wait for a CT scan, things had become dreadfully worse and paralysis from the neck down and coma came on within a short time. The CT scan confirmed what all had feared, a fracture of a vertebra in the neck that was not visible on plain X-ray. The damaged spinal cord meant that the paralysis was permanent and everyone on the care team knew that people of that age with spinal injuries faced a dismal future leading to an early death. Young people with spinal injuries could respond to rehabilitation but older people were not so resilient, and fell victim to a host of never-ending complications. Quietly, all the staff thought the lack of consciousness was a blessing under the circumstances and had begun preparing the family to accept a removal from life-support.

Of course it did not help that Mr. H.B. was occupying the last stretcher in Emergency, which made the ward unable to handle one more critical patient. The tertiary Spinal Cord Unit at the downtown hospital was overloaded already at five patients over capacity. There was little hope of moving to an ICU bed, since these were more than full, the nurses already handling two more than their usual capacity. If ICU did open another bed, priority should rightfully go to one of the two patients still in the post-operative recovery area who had developed post-surgical complications and could not be taken off their ventilators because the operating room was otherwise effectively shut down with nowhere to put people after their surgery. Without admitting it openly, the staff in Emergency was glad that their patient would be dying soon so that their last stretcher would be operational again.

And that was what made this a distressing case. Just as the family had come to accept a withdrawal of life-support, Mr. H.B. had, for mysterious reasons, woken up. He was still *paralysed and that would not change. Nor would his short future change. He was still facing a series of complications that would lead to early and certain death, all the while confined to a bed and able to move only his facial muscles while he waited for the end. Who would choose to continue if they knew what lay ahead?*

But continue he must. No one was prepared to 'pull the plug' now that he was fully awake, even though all the staff (if not the patient and family) understood clearly where that future led. The struggle to keep Emergency open would continue. The costs would somehow be borne by the system.

Euthanasia would, without a doubt, be one of the most effective of cost-saving measures in health care. It happens, however, to be illegal—not to mention immoral. This turned out to be an extremely expensive case, as all spinal injuries are, requiring a host of support services. In this particular example, it would all be for no real purpose, since the futility of rehabilitation in this age group is well established. When placed in a position with such a moral no-win, hospital staff simply will not do what is financially the most sensible thing to do. Instead, they will do what they have been taught and provide the support people are seeking. It is this fact, whether in this setting, or with the terminally ill, with the demented, and with the elderly, that pushes our costs, and creates the statistics leading to the statement that led this section.

I want to begin by thanking you for what you have done for my mother so far. It has been over four months since she was admitted and the nurses and doctors have been wonderful. She still complains about the pain in her sides, but now that we know she has cancer of the bone marrow, she is less worried about using the morphine to control the pain.

I am writing today because the doctor has started pressuring my mother to agree to stopping her kidney dialysis. My mother heard the doctor telling the nursing staff that the situation is not getting any better, so she should die. My mother was in tears when she heard this, and we are all very angry.

Mom is not in a coma. She is completely alert and has never expressed a wish to die. We see her every day and this news has completely shattered her will to live. This is not a decision that a doctor should make.

Yesterday, I was called at home by the social worker, who tried to tell me it was too long to wait until my sister's baby is born. "Why not pull the plug now?" she asked me. "If you do it now, before the new baby is born, your sister can deal with the new baby instead of with your mom."

My mom has not made peace with herself yet, and is not ready to die. She wants to be alive long enough to see the new baby, and my sister wants her to be there, too. She deserves that much, doesn't she? After 82 years of paying taxes, she finally is getting something out of the system. Please let her stay on the dialysis at least until the new baby is born.

Do we want a system that embodies compassion, even when it costs money? Or do we want one that marches to a more actuarial rhythm and ignores the human side? Whatever the answer, this is hardly a question that can be left to front-line health-care staff, nurses and physicians. Yet this is exactly what the current system does when it prescribes a rigid budget with no ability to respond to actual need. No wonder we are burning out our health-care workers at an alarming rate.

The observation that we spend most of our money at the end of life is a valid one, but it is also a natural consequence of the fact that illness generally precedes death, and illness care is what this industry is all about. The notion that this somehow presents us with an opportunity to save money is just another cruel illusion.

6. THE FEAR OF TWO-TIERED MEDICINE

There are few words more capable of arousing the anger of Canadians than these, which conjure up visions of two different line-ups, one for the rich and another for the poor. So powerful is the image gnawing at our Canadian sense of fair play, that it can be conveniently used to block all discussion and drown out the evidence that there are already many ways to circumvent the line-up. Slightly more complex—and therefore generally relegated to the garbage heap—is the question of why we need to have a line-up in the first place. Much the way Senator McCarthy in the U.S. used the word "communist" to frighten the hordes and pursue his evil agenda, the words "two-tiered medicine" have become the battle cry of the susceptible and uninformed. Even ideas that assure common waiting criteria but explore other methods of service delivery are shouted down because they might be the "thin edge of the wedge." If the politicians wanted to fortify the wall around us that keeps us beholden to their plan, they could not have chosen more wisely. It has been a highly effective tactic.

Think about it. If there are no alternatives for us to choose from, then we will have no reference point for judging quality. That means the public system can be denigrated without fear of consequence, since not only do we have no alternatives, we have no way of telling when the quality (or the delay) has exceeded reasonable proportions. If the politicians that devised medicare wanted to keep us ignorant, they would have wanted us to have nothing to compare to.

A more familiar example can be found in the retail business. The only way we have of knowing if a particular retail store is giving us an inferior deal is to watch the number of people who are choosing one of their competitors. When the law forbids any competition at all—such as in Canadian medicare—neither the consumers of health care nor the regulators have any way of knowing when services are substandard. Professional groups try to do this job but cannot. For example, the cancer society has standards for what constitutes a minimum acceptable delay to treatment once the diagnosis of cancer is made. The standard, which used to be three weeks, became eroded to six weeks, and now has become so long that its value as an alarm is virtually nil.

Can you believe it? Just when she thought she had it made. Her business is booming, they have money in the bank and the kids are moving out this summer to go to university.

I thought 52 was too young to have breast cancer, but I guess not. Did you know that her doctor told her she would have to wait six weeks just for the biopsy? Who in their right mind would wait six weeks if someone tells you that you might have cancer? Maybe someone who can't afford to do otherwise, but not anyone else. So her business and everything goes on hold. And they had that trip planned to Mexico that they cancelled. Lucky she knew that surgeon who could do her biopsy the next day. What did she have to pay to get into the private clinic? Whatever it was couldn't have been as bad as putting your life on hold for six weeks. And then what was she supposed to do, wait another six weeks after that to get her cancer surgery?

They say it was a two-and-a-half centimetre lump. What's that like, almost the size of the end of your thumb? And they say these tumours double their size in a couple of months. Wow, that means she would have lost any chance of a cure, doesn't it? What was the point of doing it at all, then?

Makes you think, doesn't it? What would I do if I had a breast lump? Would I wait six weeks and twiddle my thumbs while the chance to save my life slips away? No way. I do feel

sorry for those other poor people who can't afford any alterna-
tive, but how am I helping any of them by following the pack?

It is more than simply about our right to make a choice. What
all the arguments—both for and against private health care—have
missed is that there is no other indicator of how good or how bad our
public system really is. Waiting for statistics on death rates or on
excessive line-ups simply doesn't work and takes much too long. The
simplest way to hold our public system to account for maintaining
some level of quality in service is simply to count the number of
people who choose something else. By outlawing other alternatives in
this country, we make the U.S. health-care system accessible only to
those who can afford it, and effectively the only alternative. We fool
no one, protect no one, lose potential health care dollars to another
country, and as if that weren't bad enough, we give up the only indicator of quality within our public system that we might have had.

But try to use that or any other argument in a discussion. It
won't work. No argument is powerful enough to overcome the
non-rational force that now dominates the agenda, and that is fear.
This is why we have become immobilized and unable to come up
with a solution to our own health-care problems. If it were a
problem of a more technical nature—say, designing a super-com-
puter, or a better aircraft, or train—Canada would stand a fair
chance of success. When we are discussing our own identity in an
atmosphere filled with uncertain fears, we don't stand a chance.

7. DAMN THE TORPEDOES:

In January 2002, a group of health care experts under the auspices
of the Tommy Douglas Research Institute released a report
claiming that there was "no crisis" in Canadian health care, and
that the real enemy remained the "greedy doctors" who stood to
gain from conversion to two-tiered health care. They made a series

of recommendations they claimed would improve the situation. Some of the recommendations contained in the report were:

- Pay doctors a salary and scrap the fee-for-service system, which fosters over-reliance on doctors, drains resources, and fails to reward doctors who spend time with patients.

- Decrease the number of acute-care hospital beds, which are still used more than needed.

- Require more physicians to work in 24-hour a day group practices, especially in underpopulated, underserviced areas.

- Make better, more efficient use of Canada's existing supply of physicians, which is not as severely depleted as it has been made out to be.

- Rely more on nurse practitioners and other health professionals who can perform the more routine duties of doctors.

One thing the report failed to note was that during the past ten years, the same group of 'experts' had the ears of many of the politicians and health-care power brokers in the country. As a consequence, their counsel convinced governments to cut funding to hospitals and enrollment to medical schools, and so was responsible for creating the current shortages. They anticipated no reaction whatever to the institution of their plans, but worked instead with a model in which people simply did what they were told. They neglected to mention that forcing physicians to change how they practice was a most effective way to further reduce the number of physicians who remain here.

In other words, their advice was to ignore the evidence and continue what they had started. They wanted to entrench us even further within the *Dominant Model*. If we were to follow that advice, it would:

- Further trim the number of doctors still working in Canada, and those who did stay would be the ones enjoying leaving their clinics when their eight-hour shifts were over, minus the time taken for lunch and coffee breaks. They could, of course, expect generous benefits with their salaries, comparable to what other government workers receive.

- Salaried physicians would not use their own offices. They would need government-built-and-operated clinics, eliminating the private investment in offices and staff. After paying for the buildings, tax money left over would go to pay the union wages and job security benefits for the required number of nurses and other staff.

- The reduced number of primary care doctors (or GPs) could be replaced with nurses doing similar functions for less pay. But where do we find nurses when we cannot staff our hospitals now? Would nurses doing the doctors' work be happy with the pay they are receiving now, or would they demand a raise commensurate with their new responsibilities? Would office maintenance, support staff and other overhead all be paid directly out of taxes?

- Even if the GPs were successfully replaced, who would do the work of specialists? Would nurses also do the surgery? There are not enough surgeons now to meet the demand of patients arriving through emergency. Where do the specialists come from if doctors are encouraged to move away?

- Just as important as what their paper says is what it doesn't say. Not a word about accountability. Not a hint about consumer satisfaction or choice. Not a word about attracting expertise in medicine.

That was a year ago, and well before the two major federal reports by Kirby and Romanow were released. It is worth noting the similarity between these recommendations and the ones later that same year by the Romanov Commission.

The Final Diagnosis

Canadian medicare is not just a health system, but a system designed for political purposes, both in its inception and in its day-to-day administration. Its initial successes made its original promise seem more credible but had more to do with an advantage that came with size and legislative authority. Since then it has passed milestone after milestone on the road toward financial ruin, without anyone in control risking their neck to save it. It continues as it began, resting on the three legs of vested interest: those professional groups who stand to gain from assured paycheques, those governments that continue to farm it for political advantage, and the gullible public who have made it an icon synonymous with their national identity. After it has satisfied these voracious needs, and if it has any energy left, the system tries to look after our sick and injured.

Thirty or so years of this have left us a legacy of political interference, sanctioned financial irresponsibility, and a coven of groups with entrenched interests. The medium-term result was a provider-driven system that rendered its consumers powerless, as evidenced by the interminable waiting lists for even simple routine services. The longer-term result was the creation of shortages in just about every resource group, from nurses and physicians to pharmacists, and cardiology and laboratory technicians. These shortages are much more difficult to fix, because they create exorbitant costs for overtime, burn out the staff left on the job, and turn the waiting-list problem from a linear to an exponential one. Correcting the shortages promises to be an extremely costly business, requiring pay increases in the 30- to 50-percent range just to maintain status quo, and before any real gains are made. The last stage is one we are entering now, with a catastrophic loss of staff and a meltdown of the very institutions, which are charged with the task of providing our precious care. The decline has been slow and predictable, but the end-game will become more like a precipice than a slope. Once the people and the institutions start to go, it will be a difficult process to correct, if indeed it can ever be corrected at all.

The added weight of fulfilling the political obligations is what has made our system unstable. We can afford—or should be able to afford—looking after the health-care needs of our own population. But to do this and fulfill a political dream at the same time is too much to expect. If we want the system to survive, we must choose what it is we really want it to do. Our options are simple—either let it follow a natural course to its inevitable demise, accepting the resulting toll of human misery that we have already started, or intervene and alter the course. It is hard enough to devise a system that does one job, not two.

Unfortunately, the information needed to undo the damage is long ago lost, covered with a maze of half-baked management fads and uncompleted projects. And the correction must be led, of course, by our politicians—the very ones who have created the mess in the first place. No wonder so many conferences and discussion groups on the future of health care have been unable to come up with a consensus. The Kirby and Romanow reports suggested two very different approaches to achieve what both agreed was a common end, the saving of Medicare. More importantly, a major feature of the Kirby report, which dealt with the introduction of markets instead of global budgets, went almost completely unnoticed by the national press, which chose instead to focus on the more familiar themes of the proposed tax hike, and the "threat" posed by private interests. We remain firmly entrenched in the *Dominant Model* because it is the only one we know.

And so the analogy to the Berlin Wall takes its shape. Canadians are being held to an ideology that has little to do with their actual health, and more to do with the social-political theories of their masters. They are caught between the vested interests that each professional group enjoys in the risk-free environment of the public purse, and the politicians who ride the wave of popular appeal fuelled by tax dollars.

Just as control over the media and over public thought was important in East Berlin, so it is in Canada. Any semblance of private health care is aggressively attacked in a posture of self-righteousness, but the real reason is to make sure Canadians stay unaware of what they are missing. And just in case they ever stroll too close to the limits of what is permitted by the ideology, the rigidity of the Wall itself appears, in the guilt and accusations of the "two-tiered" argument, and this will keep them back. A physical wall it is not, but a wall of ideas it certainly is, and that can be just as much of a confinement.

There is no doubt that finally Canadians are straining against that wall. Opinion polls now show an even split—or sometimes even a small majority—in favour of alternatives to public health care. All Canadians face the same dilemma—do we stay inside the Wall and try harder to make the old ideology work, or do we try something else? Do we build the Wall even higher to contain the dissidents, or do we break it down and curse the limitations it has placed on us?

Pogo said it best in the comic strip: *"We have seen the enemy, and they is us!"*

THE PRESCRIPTION

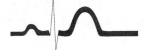

Getting the Medicine Right

The point to understand is that our hospitals are the most affected by the perverse incentives of the *Dominant Model*, and therefore make up the sickest sector of our health-care system. This is where we will need to go when we become seriously ill, but this is also the sector that is eating up the lion's share of our costs (over a third of our health spending goes directly to acute hospitals). Instead of trying to solve all of the ills of health care at the same time, our attention should go first to the part that is in most imminent danger of collapse. It might help to know that a good portion of the other ailments in health care are directly related to hospital inadequacies. The burden on doctors' offices, for example, increases because they are unable to get access to hospital beds. If the hospitals could somehow be fixed tomorrow, a good deal of the other difficulties in health care would also be solved.

The vision, then, is to replace this *Dominant Model* method of funding hospitals with something else—something that responds to market forces, and by implication, to the sick and needy who need its services. Instantly, some people will recoil at what they perceive to be the only alternative, unbridled free enterprise. But this is not the case—there *is* another alternative.

That alternative is to create an *internal market* for health care, one that mimics the feedback systems inherent in market economics, while operating within a protected environment designed to meet the overall objectives set by government. In a sense, such a system would have it all over the Americans. It would capture the best of a market economy, while retaining the central direction and open information systems that the Americans can only dream of. This is because we already have, in government, one dominant player that can set both the rules of engagement and the prices, then let the internal market do its work to get the best possible deal for taxpayers. Americans are burdened with hundreds of different insurance companies that answer to no one, and an open-ended market policy that sustains itself by driving utilization, forcing the total cost beyond what is reasonable or necessary. By marrying our public system with the principles of market economics, we can do better.

Remember the last meeting of COMECON, at the beginning of this book, and think of how irrelevant that group had become to the events that followed. Instead of more five-year-plans formulated by people in closed rooms, we need a new set of rules that harness natural market forces and reward for services provided instead of rewarding the act of sending people away. An internal market would do this *within the context of a public system* simply by placing clear values on the services we want our public to have, by rewarding initiative and success, and by penalizing those who are unable to produce those services at a competitive price.

Bringing back the ugly word "competition" into health care may seem anathema to some, but it is the best way to control our costs and preserve our services at the same time. In a sense, the timing is right for change, because almost no one wants to continue as we are, and almost anything is preferable to the alternative of letting our public system crumble in the dust.

Change, however, is easier said than done. If we did want to make such a change, where would we start?

The remainder of this chapter lists TEN steps designed around the theme of an internal market that could rescue our hospitals and form the basis for a sustainable public health system for our country. As Tom Peters once said, when fixing a problem, it is always wise to start at the top.

1. HEALTH CARE IS NOT FREE

When we ask schoolchildren about the difference between living in Canada and living in the U.S., one of the more likely responses is "It's better to live in Canada, because health care here is free."

Health care is not now—nor has it ever been—free. Adults may know this on an intellectual level, but everything in our behaviour points otherwise. This simple point lies at the heart of the dilemma Canadians face. We must stop pretending that health care in Canada is free.

The Canada Health Act is ostensibly there to guarantee us all access, yet the best-known and most-threatening provision is the one that prescribes financial penalties to provinces that allow extra-billing. The public seems to overlook the fact that nothing about this clause improves access to anyone, anywhere. What it addresses is how health care is paid for, and its purpose is to perpetuate the perceived myth that health care is free. If it were acknowledged to be otherwise, health care would lose its political value. If the Act needs to impose any penalties at all, they should be for denial of access, not for a mechanism for payment that is agreeable to both parties. Of course, penalizing lack of access could be more difficult, since unreasonable waits for medical care are really just another form of denial of access.

There are two reasons we must stop pretending health care is free. The first is to stop it from continuing to be used as a political football. And the second is so that realistic discussions on alternative funding methods can begin before a complete financial collapse of the present system occurs.

2. TAKE THE POLITICS OUT OF HEALTH CARE

Politicians have a legitimate role in assigning priorities for tax money, defining objectives, and monitoring progress toward those objectives. They have no business trying to micromanage health delivery systems or playing games with resources. The best way to remove politicians from that process is to remove the possibility of political gain by making the funding of health care independent from other government operations.

All provincial governments currently bury their health-care budgets within general revenue. That means it is impossible to tease out what money goes where, and impossible to assign overall financial accountability. No wonder the public does not trust politicians. This mixing of health-care funds with all other government accounts makes a shell game of any attempt to be fiscally responsible.

Will politicians readily relinquish what is currently one of their most powerful ways of gaining the limelight? Probably not. But it would help if the public, especially the press, began demonstrating that they are onto the game, and began to call them on it.

The Patient Care Contract

Traditional medicine teaches doctors they have an obligation to their patients. Whether one relies on the Hippocratic oath or not, doctors and patients have an implied contract in which the doctor undertakes to be honourable, protect the confidentiality of the patient, and as much as possible, to act in the patient's best interests. For a fee, of course. But the fee paid in exchange cements the contractual nature of the relationship, because both parties must have a gain in order for there to be a "contract." The value of contracts is that when something goes wrong, the contract defines clearly who is responsible. When a patient's care fails to meet his expectations, it is the contractor (the doctor) who must correct the situation.

The advent of government as a major player changes all of this. In a simple insurance situation, the insurer merely agrees to compensate for the loss, but the ownership of the fault does not change. However, when a government forms a medical plan that dictates how care will proceed and pays the doctor as well as the others involved in the provision of care, it is no longer clear who is taking over the contract with the patient. It is this lack of clarity that creates a serious problem, since it is no longer obvious who is responsible to fix things when they go wrong.

In fact, one could go so far as to say that both major participants in medicare—the doctor and the government—have different concepts of who is the major contractor and who is merely a sub-contractor. Most doctors still think they are the ones who contract with their own patients and they are the ones responsible. Most administrators and politicians have quite a different view, and would feel they are the ones with the responsibility of protecting the public, and the doctors are mere hirelings in the process.

The reason why doctors are singled out here, rather than nurses and other health professionals, is because it is still the doctor we expect to make the major decisions about the course of care. We expect the doctor to make the diagnosis of brain tumour and tell us we need surgery. We want a doctor to tell us if it is appendicitis and if surgery is really necessary. It is the doctor who decides that this headache is from a brain aneurysm and advises us what the best course of treatment would be. Once the decision is made, a cascade of events occurs that involves a host of other staff, but few people are ready to have anyone other than a qualified physician make that critical first decision.

Just who is really on the other end of the contract–physician or health service—remains a major stumbling point, rarely even discussed within the context of medicare systems in Canada. It is not so much my concern which it should be, rather the lack of even a discussion on the matter, which is the problem. Our American friends are more careful about such liability issues. In the case of large HMOs such as Kaiser Health, it is definitely the organization as a whole that is responsible, and people are clearly told that when they sign on. The doctors who work for such firms understand this also, take on a lower level of responsibility, and accept the orders given by the organization. And when something goes wrong, the organization is the one that (hopefully) accepts the blame and the responsibility to fix the problem. The situation in Canada is much less clear. Doctors and government argue constantly about control over the system, without addressing the fundamental issues of responsibility, and with no resolution in sight.

Why does this matter? Because if responsibility is left undefined and unclear, then no one is responsible for fixing things if they go wrong. Doctors argue they cannot, hampered with shortages of basic commodities like hospital beds and operating room time. Governments, on the other hand, insist doctors must make do within their allocated budgets, and have a long line of arguments to support their contention that there is enough money in the system, if only the doctors would use it better. The missing voice is that of the patient, and of the millions of Canadians who will some day find they have become sick. No one has even asked them who they trust and with whom they want to be making their contract.

3. REGIONALIZE THE DELIVERY OF HEALTH CARE

Throughout these chapters, we have assumed that health care is delivered by a "Region" rather than by an individual hospital. The word is used as a short form to mean "Regional Health Authority" or sometimes simply 'RHA.' Briefly, this is an entity created to manage the health care within a defined geographical region. Many provinces have regionalized their health care, but not all. Those that have not are left with a collage of hospitals, varying in size, organizational structure, and effectiveness. All of them, since they operate in a public-only system, are completely dependent on governments for their money, but are too small to exert any significant influence of their own, or to experiment across a broad category of services. They become not unlike a network of fill-up stations, geographically situated to be convenient for a certain community of people, but with little or no discretion to change anything. The advantage is that they can do little else than obey their political and bureaucratic masters, who make all the key decisions in the health ministry.

Regionalization changes this. Regions are usually defined initially by government on a geographical basis, but incorporate a unified management structure that includes several hospitals, community health clinics and long-term care centres. For starters, an RHA is usually large enough to gain economies of scale on several fronts, including purchasing, planning, and administration. The necessity of operating several hospitals also ensures that a mix of different levels of care is represented within each region, promoting co-operation between hospitals. The RHA should also be large enough to experiment, to some extent, with health-delivery systems other than the ones inherited by them. In a typical model, not all RHAs would be equally successful, but the less successful ones would quickly learn from their more robust cousins and the competitive environment would spur improvement.

Perhaps the most important strength of regionalization is the ability of the RHA to take on an advocacy role on behalf of their constituents. Provincial ministries are too large to do this in a believable way, and also become adversaries because of their necessary role as guardian of the money. Individual hospitals may become advocates also, but are usually too narrow in their scope to support such a role across the broad spectrum of services required, especially if they are constantly scrambling for money.

Of course, regionalization itself is not a guarantee of success. RHAs that are too large must force cooperation across too many disparate communities, lose their cohesiveness, and spend too much time trying to keep peace in a "family" that has little in common. They also fail to make believable advocates for patients faced with impersonal bureaucracies little different than the original ministry of health.

On the other hand, RHAs that are too small fail to achieve the critical mass necessary to reach economies of scale, and cannot provide a broad spectrum of services, constantly relying instead on neighbouring RHAs to help them out. RHAs that have governance models imposed on them, aimed at achieving political ends, reach predictable stalemates in all aspects of their operations. And finally, RHAs that are not given adequate control of their funds lose the flexibility required to do anything at all, and become larger fill-up stations with no autonomy of their own. They might as well have remained individual hospitals under central ministry control. It would have been less expensive.

Nevertheless, it is my own conviction that regionalization—if properly done, with adequate independence and financial authority—offers a vibrant system of public health care that combines the competitive spirit of private enterprise with the stability and comfort of public medicare. Appropriately constituted, RHAs have the potential to be large enough to provide a broad spectrum of services, achieve cost efficiencies of scale, and create co-operative arrangements across different disciplines. Most importantly, they should be large enough to be trusted with authority on capital budgets, while at the same time they need to be small enough to believably represent the interest of individuals and respond to local needs.

4. EXPERIMENT WITH HOW PRIMARY CARE IS DELIVERED (BUT DON'T EXPECT TO SAVE ANY MONEY)

Just listen to the usual advice on health-care restructuring that comes from governments and so-called experts. Much of it is spent on finding ways to restrict the public's access to primary-care doctors. There is a common impression that people run to their doctors for all kinds of minor complaints, such as colds and flus, thereby pushing health-care costs higher with their irresponsible actions. The ideas vary from paying family doctors by salary, to decrease their incentive to keep people coming in (thereby also guaranteeing that the number of doctors available will plummet further), to forcing people to see a nurse practitioner first. The frenzy is fuelled by studies showing that a large percentage of primary care visits are for colds and other self-limiting disease.

As we discussed in an earlier chapter, what is not so well known is that most of the statistics on which this is based come from billing diagnosis codes. In many provinces, doctors must put down a numeric code that describes the diagnosis. Most patient complaints are really more multi-factorial, but in order to get paid, the doctor must choose only one diagnosis. Since there seems to be no consequence to which diagnosis is chosen, doctors tend to re-use the same codes they are most familiar with and use them as a kind of grab bag so they can get on with their other work. Naturally, the diagnosis is one made after the examination. Patients rarely know exactly what they have; otherwise, they wouldn't be seeing the doctor. The most difficult aspect of medical practice is the knowledge that somewhere in the middle of the 'haystack' of common complaints will lie the 'needle' of someone with a critical illness. Failing to understand that simple point often leads our 'experts' to conclude that a real doctor is only needed a small fraction of the time. In reality, the opposite is true, because it is finding the illness among the host of common complaints that represents the true skill of a competent physician.

A similar situation occurs with emergency departments, as we have already seen. It may be true in retrospect that a significant number of people could have been treated elsewhere, but the act of finding that out is the true function of the emergency department. In that case, it has been shown that trying to eliminate the 'minor' complaints from Emergency does serious harm to a small but consistent subset of patients, while failing to address the major headache all emergency departments face—where to put the patients who are truly sick.

All of these approaches to changing primary care miss one simple point. As a proportion of the total health care budget, all physicians' fees typically represent only about 18 percent of the total bill. Roughly half of this goes to specialists, and the rest goes to primary care physicians of all kinds. In other words, all of our general practitioners currently cost us less than nine percent of our health care budget. Even a huge saving in this one segment—say, an across the board reduction of 20 percent—would still only amount to less than two percent of our total budget. Even a minor deterioration in referral patterns to specialists that might result in such a re-organization—for example, if nurse practitioners referred more cases to specialists—would quickly eat up even that small saving.

Any reasonable approach to saving health-care dollars would come to the conclusion that primary care itself is simply not worth the cost of re-organizing. Considering the hours spent, the unrestricted access, and the level of expertise provided, the money we now spend on primary care is well worth it. Any significant reductions in costs has to come not from physicians' incomes per se, but from a decrease in utilization of in-hospital resources, the majority of which is under the control of physicians who are specialists.

That doesn't mean better ways don't exist of reaching people and increasing effectiveness. On the contrary, innovations should be encouraged. My point is that the outcome should be concerned with public satisfaction and effective health delivery rather than with saving money. In fact, the most recent research on methods of primary-care delivery shows there are advantages and disadvantages to all methods, with some being more effective with specific types of populations, but that none of the methods (including salaries and capitation) are inherently less expensive than the others.

It is an ideal area for experimentation, which should be encouraged both regionally and between provinces. One of the best ways to measure outcome is to let the various approaches compete for public satisfaction and service.

There is one thing, however, that we need no research to show, and that should be done with general practice. That is the extra burden general practitioners carry when they care for their in-hospital patients. We have already seen the current crisis driving general practitioners out of their hospitals and into the walk-in clinics. The trend threatens to leave us without GPs who are prepared to care for patients ill enough to be in hospital. Governments need to address this issue by adjusting the compensation to reward the behaviour they want to encourage. One way would be to pay a premium rate on all fees billed by GPs who maintain their hospital privileges in good standing. This would finally give hospitals the teeth they need to enforce proper practice, such as ensuring in-hospital patients are visited by their GP each day.

Doctors should be free, of course, to give up their hospital privileges if they choose to do so. There may be many reasons for doing this, but their fees should be lowered to reflect the fact that they have chosen a less onerous pattern of practice. Many patients do not even know whether their family doctor has hospital privileges or where he practices, and assume somehow that their GP will be there for them when they need him. This, of course, is far from true. The principle of proper disclosure should require family physicians to display, in a prominent location in their offices, the hospitals in which they maintain active privileges, and if they choose not to have an in-hospital practice, to clearly state that fact.

One of the weaknesses of the fee-for-service style of practice is that all physicians who do the same procedure bill the same amount, regardless of their experience, expertise, and their choice of practice location. Those, for instance, who choose to practice in a remote community receive the same fee as those who choose a major city already filled with doctors. Some provinces address this inequity by offering an extra fee for practicing in remote or northern locations. This is fine, but only addresses part of the problem, since the same fees are still in place all across the province.

In actual fact, need varies with local conditions, some communities needing a radiologist more than a surgeon, and so on. The desirability of living and working in one community or other also varies. To some extent, having a provincial fee schedule distorts the incentives by forcing one solution on all the communities.

Looking outside of health care, for example, communities that need the services of a priest or minister often conduct their own searches and offer local incentives, such as a home, or a rent reduction, or other attractions, in addition to pay. This allows some competition to come into play, letting both the priest and the community find the best solution for their own needs. The same solution could operate in health care except for the interference of the provincial government, which, being a common player, has no alternative but to impose the same settlement on all. Allowing some form of market to operate in health-care manpower forms the core of another problem in health care that we will address next.

5. PAY ESSENTIAL STAFF WHAT IT TAKES

What is the best way to deal with staff—be they doctors, nurses, or technicians—when they refuse to do their jobs unless their exorbitant demands are met? This is the question that hospital administrators, politicians, and health ministry staff are asking each other today. The issue has been thrust into centre stage by numerous doctor boycotts and threats. Solving one seems only to open up the next one a few months later somewhere else. A more permanent approach to dealing with these crises is what everyone on the management side of the industry is looking for.

Some advocate the negotiating process. This would be fine, except that all of our current agreements are already the result of a negotiating process, and often result in a work disruption even under a current valid contract. Re-opening negotiations is an admission that the former process did not work, at the same time as it becomes superseded by a newer version of the same process. The message is that other workers also have permission to re-open their contracts and threaten job action if their demands are not met. The "Prince George syndrome," named after the successful walkout in northern British Columbia in the spring of 2000, is the cynical name applied to the situation in which one renegotiated contract leads to a chain reaction of "me-too" disruptions. The situation is being repeated over and over in many communities, and is no longer restricted to remote locations.

Some advocate unionizing the doctors, since unions (unlike the professional associations doctors use) have the power defined in legislation to discipline their members and enforce a collective agreement. Those advocating this approach conveniently ignore the fact that the same disruptions have also been occurring even within the union framework, in the case of perfusionists, lab workers, and even nurses, many of whom have now learned to turn down work unless overtime rates are being paid.

Still others advocate the "hardball" approach, in which workers who make such threats are fired outright, or in the case of doctors, their hospital privileges are cut off. This approach works very well in situations in which the workers are not really needed. It is, of course a disaster when they are desperately needed, and especially so when there is a shortage so that no one else is available to take their place.

What many health-care managers are learning very quickly is that—as long as the worker is truly indispensable, of course—the best way to win at hardball is to call on the line-up of other workers with equal qualifications ready and willing to take their place. This is precisely the reason one should avoid shortages in the first place, and the reason why, when a shortage does occur, that there is no alternative to giving in and paying what it takes. Doing otherwise threatens to make the shortage even worse, further weakening bargaining power. This is just as true inside a union environment as out.

One can readily understand that the collective bargaining model was developed over the past century in blue-collar industries and was successful precisely because these groups had little mobility. The same model never worked as well with professionals and white-collar workers, because they have always been relatively more mobile. In today's fast-paced economy, all people can move more readily, and nurses are certainly among the more mobile of workers. Collective agreements simply cannot be enforced when people can pick up and move to another jurisdiction with better pay—at least, not without much more physical intimidation than our society will tolerate.

The greatest threat to keeping our health care alive right now is the shortage of staff, especially nurses. The result of any shortage is a dramatic rise in cost, as those still on the job work extra hard, for longer hours, to compensate for the difficulty attracting staff. This compensation has been going on for many years, but now has reached the point where compensation is no longer possible. Governments that have been relying on salary ceilings for years, in an attempt to hold the line on budgets, are now finding that the technique has backfired and is causing salary increases that appear out of control. The more they resist, the worse the shortage gets, the more staff get angry and leave for other less stressful or higher-paying opportunities. And so we fuel the vicious cycle.

But raises in pay are only a short-term solution, of course. The longer-term answer must be to increase the supply of workers. In the case of both nurses and doctors, this means nothing less than a reversal of the policies our politicians have pursued for the past decade. Considering that it takes at least four years to increase the supply of nurses through the increase in training seats, we might expect to see a few apologetic politicians anxiously attempt to make up for their past mistakes.

It is an unlikely scenario. In the short run, there is no way around the problem other than to accept the increased costs of labour and learn from our mistakes. The sooner we do this, the sooner we can reverse the threat of disintegration on our doorstep. We must accept at face value the rising cost of getting nurses, who are now in short supply, as the spilt milk of our previous policies.

Unfortunately, that's not so easily done when one considers how most hospital workers, including nurses, are paid. Except for excluded staff and physicians, all hospital workers are paid salaries set by a collective bargaining process. That means everyone has to wait until the existing contract has expired and new negotiations have concluded before anything can be done. Then the perception is that we have to fend off what will appear to be exorbitant expectations. Since labour agreements are always measured by percent increase from the previous contract, this round of negotiations will seem extraordinary, indeed. There is always a "drag effect," which simply put, is the reluctance of employers to give percentage increases that are too high relative to the previous contract for fear of raising hopes of other bargaining groups waiting their turn.

What it all means is that, whatever the final negotiated salary turns out to be, it will probably not be enough to catch up with the true spread between demand and supply, especially if things get worse during the term of the next contract. The new contract will instead raise the floor, which is helpful for the nurse, but it will continue to impose an inability to respond to local shortages. In the end, nurses will be making more money, but will still be over-worked and unsatisfied with their jobs, and therefore will remain poised to leave, aggravating the situation further. As we have seen already, collective agreements were originally designed for a captive workforce. In the setting of one that is more mobile, they tend to create shortages or make them worse rather than better.

There is an alternative. While collective agreements are a legitimate way to protect basic salaries and ensure proper working conditions, they were never intended to limit the pay increases of individual workers. Most contracts do not, in fact, specifically prevent the employer from paying more, but they still inhibit the practice through intimidation. This is unfortunate, because an employer who offers a bonus over and above the contract wage to attract workers to key positions and encourage them to stay there will satisfy the worker, harm no one, and keep the operation running—thereby protecting other workers' jobs.

The key in the short run to breaking the deadlock of staff shortages, is to accept the increased cost as an inescapable consequence of foolish past practices, and to do so early by offering immediate pay bonuses beyond those specified in the contract. It implies a recognition that working with an under-supply of staff is already more expensive, further increasing costs as patients pile up in the wait-lists and corridors. The sooner this can be reversed, the less the overall pain and cost to the organization will be, and the more motivated workers will be to meet the overall aims of the organization. In the longer run, a new and different process is set to potentially overtake collective bargaining as a way of determining wages. It is based on the value of the end product.

6. END GLOBAL BUDGETS: PAY FOR PRODUCTS, NOT PROCESSES

Instead of paying for a finished product or for services provided, the global budget mechanism used for hospital funding pays for processes once thought necessary to achieve that product. A hospital may succeed in getting a paediatric unit funded. Another will obtain money for a diabetic clinic. Still another might start a home intravenous program. These processes tend to start off with good intentions, but often get mired within their own needs and system problems.

Unfortunately, within the public service, processes that start off getting funded generally continue to get funded, regardless of whether they are still providing the intended service or not. More often some service continues to be provided, not in the quantity originally planned, but without any effect on the original amount of funding. The long-term result is a patchwork of well-intended processes, each claiming importance, but with varying success at actually delivering something real that consumers still want. Untangling the mess is a formidable task and it is easier just to continue funding based on history.

While it may be necessary sometimes to provide start-up funding to get some processes going—especially if they are enabling to some other aspects of care—long-term funding should be tied to services actually provided rather than to processes. This would ensure three things: (a) that the process remains true to its original aims, (b) it allows payment to be adjusted to the volume of cases, something that is not always easy to predict at the start, and (c) if someone can think of a less expensive way to provide the same product, it would replace the original process.

Funding for actual product or services is the universal rule in almost every industry, and in almost every country. The glaring exception is Canadian hospital care. Why are hospitals in Canada treated so differently to every other form of human economic activity?

Making the Leap to Service-Based Funding (SBF)

Perhaps the single most important step toward creating an internal market for hospitals is to change from the current global budget method of hospital funding to some form of SBF. Service Based Funding means that instead of paying hospitals a global budget calculated by the health ministry to meet their anticipated needs, they are paid according to what they actually do. In other words, money follows patient services. That, of course, means we have to make a list of in-hospital services that we want to pay for, and attach a dollar value to each. Under this system, instead of simply having their budgets automatically renewed, hospitals would have to actually earn their income by delivering services. In short, they would have to work for their money just like everyone else (aside from government) has to do. Replacing global budgets for hospitals with Service Based Funding was one of the core concepts embraced by Senator Michael Kirby in his report last November, and it deserves a detailed explanation.

The current widespread practice among many of the provinces is still to simply reallocate last year's budget with a small adjustment for inflation. Some have moved to what is called 'population-based funding' (or PBF). This is simply a method of estimating, based on where people live and on what health-care resources they used last year, what their needs will be in the coming year, and proportioning out a budget to hospitals or Health-Care Regions to suit.

Population-based funding can become quite complex, with adjustments for age, sex, and sometimes socio-economic status, all of which are known determinants of health-care utilization and cost. Even so, it cannot take into account where people choose to go for their health care. Especially in urban areas, people tend to move around quite a bit for their health care. Although PBF attempts to compensate for these movements by using historical data, it can never give more than an educated guess what will happen in the current year. Perhaps its greatest weakness is the built-in assumption that the previous year's utilization—on which it builds—accurately reflects need, when in reality it is a skewed result of the previous year's allocation errors. This means that it performs best the first year it is implemented, but trails farther away from reality each year, as each projection compounds the errors of the previous year. At best, PBF can never be more than a reimbursement plan for health dollars actually spent by the hospitals in the previous year, and can never provide incentives for service. At its worst, it is a quota system dressed up as thoughtful science.

By contrast, instead of guessing at what an annual budget for a hospital or RHA will be, service-based funding (SBF) pays hospitals a fixed fee for each recognized service when that service is provided. The difference between the two, and their effects on hospitals, could not be more different.

(a) First of all, money would flow where it is actually being spent, instead of where bureaucrats think it will be spent. This matching of resources with need can never be more than a remote dream for PBF.

(b) Second, hospitals would be forced to learn and understand their cost structures. Those putting this information to good use would see a realistic chance of generating a surplus which can be reinvested into more services. Without a question, there would be some losers as well—those hospitals encountering financial difficulties in this system probably had them for some time and were able to keep them hidden. The most important people who need to know that the hospital is not competitive are the managers themselves, who are in a position to do something about it. Far from being a problem, 'exposing the losers' is a very positive step, because it is the only way something can be done to help them. Our current system has allowed them to perpetuate their practices, sometimes even without the knowledge of their own managers.

(c) Third, doctors (and also nurses and other health care professionals) would be transformed overnight, from being drains on hospital resources into valuable assets. Under the current system, hospitals must actually try to keep doctors away—or, at least, limit their numbers if they want to remain financially solvent. SBF would change this instantly, forcing the incentives to work in exactly the opposite direction. Hospitals that continued the old ways of deterring staff and limiting services they provide to patients would incur a loss of income and quickly face financial disaster.

(d) Fourth, since hospitals know their annual workload with reasonable accuracy, they would be able to predict the income they will get for their services, and that knowledge can be an incentive to invest resources and promote growth. There is nothing in the old PBF formula that acts as an incentive for growth; on the contrary, PBF was designed precisely for the purpose of limiting growth.

(e) Bed closures and cancellations of surgery would quickly become a thing of the past, because hospitals would be forced to find ways to keep patients moving to avoid a financial loss. If, for example, a surgery worth $10,000 in revenue to the hospital were threatened with cancellation because a nurse that costs $200 was not able to come to work, what should the hospital do? Under the current system, the surgery would be cancelled. Doing so under SBF would be painfully expensive. The result is that nurses would no longer have to resort to unions and strikes to get pay raises the labour market tells us they need.

(f) Last and most important of all, hospitals would no longer treat their patients as unwanted burdens. Ensuring patients are satisfied would become not just a matter of weary professional concern, it would be necessary for financial survival as well. Finally, the consumers of health care in Canada would begin to carry some power. It is long overdue.

All Those Opposed Raise Their Hands

If things were so simple, why hasn't anyone done this already? It is not difficult to see that an overnight switch to SBF would not make everyone happy. I can think of at least three groups of people who are likely to object.

The first are the "health-care planners." I use the term loosely, but by this I mean the people who believe that services can be improved and money saved by large-scale central planning. They are also the ones who continually expect people to do what they are told by their planners, and become frustrated when they act instead according to what they see as their own interests. These people abound in government ministries, but also are well represented in academics and in many hospital and RHA hierarchies.

It is only natural for these "planners" to find SBF threatening, both to their ideology, and to their careers. The fact that SBF recognizes a certain degree of market reality would raise more than a small red flag. Many find any hint of the word 'market' objectionable, as if it carried a moral value not in keeping with the lofty ideals of health care. The fact that markets carry necessary information and empower the users is not a point they like to acknowledge. In general, they think they know better than regular people.

The second are the politicians, or more accurately, those responsible for finding money to pay for health care. They are concerned because they have been told for decades (by the planners) that runaway costs in health care are the fault of hospitals and doctors who are always trying to do too much. They have also been told that more services by hospitals and doctors increases cost, but do not result in any measurable improvement in health outcomes. Naturally, the fear is a return to unlimited growth by these two power-hungry groups, and a bill for health care that breaks the bank.

The third are those people who suspect the hospital they work in would lose money under the scheme or be unable to compete, resulting in a disaster to their own jobs. While a valid concern, it is not a good reason against making the move. It is, however, a reason for careful transition, taking time for people to learn how their own organization works and how to make it better. These will be the engines for the improvements in productivity that SBF will bring.

What About the Soaring Costs of Health Care?

The concern about rising costs is one I will take more seriously. Without question, a change to SBF could result in higher costs, at least initially. Years and years of deliberate under-investment in structures, techniques and equipment cannot be turned around without facing some consequences. Backlogs of people waiting for routine procedures will not disappear unless they are finally attended to. Eventually, the consequences of the shortages we created in all aspects of our health manpower will find us and make us pay, as every one of us should have known even while these shortages were being created.

We must ask ourselves: if it became clear that health care had in fact truly been underfunded all these years, would an increase in spending not be justified?

On the other hand, we could reject SBF and simply continue what we are doing now. We fool ourselves into thinking that artificial limits placed on funds will control the cost of health care, but we are forgetting one of its most expensive aspects—something I call "queue costs." These are simply the costs directly related to maintaining the queue that results when we limit access to hospital resources. A real-life example might help make this clear.

> *Mrs. J.B. arrived in my emergency department at six a.m., complaining of abdominal pain that had kept her up all night. She had given birth three months earlier and since then had experienced an exacerbation of her gallbladder problems. Originally diagnosed by ultrasound a year earlier with gallstones, she had declined surgery at that time because she had only had a few attacks of pain, and the long waitlist had deterred her. Her doctor had agreed it would be better to wait until her pregnancy was over before she contemplated surgery.*
>
> *In the last two weeks she had had four episodes of pain, and had been seen in another emergency department the previous day, where another ultrasound was done. It, again, confirmed the presence of stones in her gallbladder. Because she was not deemed to be having a life-threatening emergency, she was sent home with Demerol tablets for pain, but was told to come back to hospital if things became worse. Of course, things were going to get worse. When I saw her, it was a Saturday and the emergency department was completely full with no spare beds. I had already referred several people with recurrent gallbladder pain to the general surgeon on call earlier in the week, but I knew all of them had been sent home. Even*

262 DIAGNOSIS AND PRESCRIPTION

though the surgeon had the ability to completely cure their pain with a one-hour procedure, he had sent them home instead because there was no hope of getting the necessary operating room time. Perhaps the surgeon had become somewhat inured, because he had a line-up of people seen through his office who had already been waiting three months or more with the same condition.

Something about this particular patient made me sympathetic, perhaps because she kept breaking into tears. I examined her but found little unusual. The pain, in fact, had gone away by the time I saw her (as it usually does), and she did not seem terribly sick.

I told her the chances of my being able to help her were small unless she was much sicker than she appeared to be. Merely having pain all the time was no longer a criterion for immediate action in our hospital. But she kept complaining that she still had a dull ache that wouldn't go away and was having trouble breast-feeding her baby, because she had been unable to eat any food for two days without vomiting. I also was suspicious that her eyes might be more yellow in colour than normal, although I couldn't be sure that it was due to jaundice. I told her that I would at least do some blood tests to make sure there was no infection or obstruction, but that if those tests were normal, I would be forced to send her home again with more Demerol. She tearfully agreed.

As it turned out, the blood tests were quite abnormal, showing not an infection, but an obstruction of the biliary tract with bile backing up into the liver. The bilirubin levels did indeed indicate that she was jaundiced, and I had been correct in my suspicions about the colour of her eyes. I told her the good news. Yes, she was indeed obstructed with a stone in her biliary tract, and that changed her status to urgent. I *would admit her to hospital, even though there were no beds and she would stay in our orthopaedic plaster room overnight. The good news was that the surgeon would be forced to do something now. Her tears became a torrent, but they were tears of joy as she told her husband the good news, that her liver was bursting with bile.*

I read her operative report a few days later. A repeat ultrasound had confirmed that one of the stones in her gallbladder had slipped down into the common bile duct, the small tube leading into her intestine, causing a high degree of obstruction to the flow of bile, and a backup of bile in the liver. Simply taking her gallbladder out would no longer solve her problem, since the gallbladder was only the source of the stone, but the stone that had travelled and was causing the problem would still be there. What she needed now was an extraction of the stone from the duct below the gallbladder.

ERCP is a technique in which a fibre-optic tube is passed down the throat into the stomach, threading it into the duodenum and visually locating the tiny Ampulla of Vater—the opening where the bile duct empties into the duodenum. The doctor then threads the tiny scope up into this opening and into the common bile duct where the stone is, locates the stone, and mechanically pulls it out. The entire procedure takes about an hour, but because it requires only some sedation and not a full anaesthetic, it did not require precious operating room time. In this patient's case, this was successfully done on the Monday, relieving her obstructed duct and correcting the urgent part of the situation.

The tragedy was that after all that, she was sent home again with her gallbladder still full of stones, to wait her turn for gallbladder removal. Instead of having one procedure and dealing with the entire problem when it first arose, she had to

put up with weeks of pain, have a different procedure done,
take up numerous doctor's visits and a hospital bed, and still
she was sent home with her original problem.

Quite aside from the humanitarian issues, how did forcing this
woman to wait with her gallbladder pain save any money? Not only
did it not save money, it cost extra for the additional visits and the
procedure that should have been unnecessary—not to mention the
personal costs her family had to bear in lost wages and time looking
after an ill family member.

It all started innocently enough as A. K. checked himself
into the local emergency department for abdominal pain. He
had awakened that morning with a mild ache, but went to
work as usual, not wanting to be one to complain too easily.
Perhaps that pizza the previous night had not been a good
idea after all. But by the afternoon, instead of feeling better,
the pain had worsened, and he had a hard time keeping
upright while walking. It was only four p.m. and seemed
better to A. K. to get it checked out now, rather than wait
until the middle of the night.

No one in the emergency department was too excited by
the presentation. Abdominal pain is one of the more common
problems that present to any ER. The triage nurse knew that
most of them go home with a benign diagnosis. Could be the
flu or something he ate. Could be constipation or just a plain
upset stomach. In this case, the diagnosis was not difficult. A
physical examination and a blood count confirmed the diag-
nosis of appendicitis. It was now 8:30 p.m.

Appendicitis is caused by a small, hardened object in the
stool that imbeds itself in the neck of the small, finger-like pro-
jection at the entrance to the large bowel. At first, the bowel

simply tries to work it out by contracting, sending waves of painful cramps to the owner of the problem. Gradually, over the next few hours, the obstruction causes local swelling that impedes the returning venous blood supply from the appendix. Much like a ring around a swollen finger, once the problem becomes established, it can only get worse, unless the obstruction is relieved. That means surgery.

But it is difficult to know for sure whether the stone will come out on its own, or whether the inflammation and swelling will progress. If that happens, the lining of the appendix breaks down, allowing the bacteria inside to invade and form an abscess which will eventually rupture—relieving the pressure, but spreading the infection further around the peritoneum, the inside of the abdominal cavity.

Because of the uncertainty in the early stages, it is not uncommon to simply wait and observe—being prepared, of course, to make the decision to operate once an acceptable threshold of certainty is reached. That is what happened in the "old days," before sophisticated imaging was available. Waiting is still useful, but ultrasound and CT scan can often give valuable early confirmation of the true diagnosis and avoid the risk of rupture.

Unfortunately, it was now out of hours and too late to get an ultrasound, and this hospital did not have a CT scanner. In order to 'rationalize' services, CT units had only been installed in selected hospitals. Patients needing CT scans had to be shipped to the larger referral hospital in the region. As it turned out that evening, the other hospital was full and could not accept a transfer. The emergency doctor decided that waiting and observing his patient overnight was not an unreasonable option, as long as surgery could take place in the morning.

It takes about 24 hours for appendicitis to progress through its various stages and reach the point of rupture. An appendectomy before rupture is a simple procedure that needs a surgeon, an operating room, and a three-day in-hospital stay. A ruptured appendix is a different matter. Although rarely fatal as it once was, it involves a longer surgery, long-term antibiotics, and a ten-day in-hospital stay or more— along with a much longer recovery time at home. The long-term complications are also significant, with internal scarring which can cause painful bowel obstructions, repeat hospital admissions, and sometimes more surgery decades later. Our patient knew none of this, and was happy at least to be in a hospital with his pain under control.

Morning came and the pain had indeed worsened, making the diagnosis look more firm. But some days have a way of taking their own direction. The referral hospital was no better off than the evening before, and after handling a trauma case from the ER, still could not accept a transfer. The surgeon accepted the case, but could not get an open operating theatre until the end of the day when more urgent cases had been done. It was time to see if a different hospital could be found. Time for the "Bedline" to spring into action.

Many provinces now have processes to look for available beds in other hospitals. Some, in Ontario, Alberta, and B.C., have sophisticated systems that use the Internet to locate empty beds when none are available in the local hospital. In this case, the system was new, but keen to help. A bed was in fact located, but not in any of the nearby hospitals. The surgery however, could be performed there, provided he could make the two-hour trip by ambulance.

It was now 2:00 p.m. and dangerously close to the end of the 24-hour envelope in which the surgery needed to be done.

But the surgeon at the accepting hospital now had a problem. He had too many experiences in which transfers had gone ahead without the referring surgeon verifying the situation. In those cases, patients had been transferred at great discomfort and cost when surgery was not even necessary. He wanted to make sure the surgeon at the originating hospital thought it was a true case of appendicitis and that he would have operated on it himself if he had a bed.

Fair enough, but the referring surgeon was now himself in the OR, operating on another urgent case, and it would take him until six p.m. to comply. Eventually, that is what happened, and the transfer ambulance was called. Mr. A.K. left the emergency department at 7:30 p.m.—almost 28 hours after he had arrived—destined for another hospital two hours away, for a routine appendectomy. The new provincial "Bedline" service would chalk it up as another "success" demonstrating their ability to find a bed when one was needed, and everyone would go about their business.

Neither of these situations is at all unusual. Both illustrate what all health care professionals have come to realize: once waiting lists reach a certain size, they no longer save money—*they actually cost **more** money*. Our waiting lists, in most of Canada, have long ago passed that critical point. Part of the reason politicians have failed to turn this around is that some of the costs are borne not by their health ministry, but by a different pot—the patient. Miniscule savings in hospital processes are subsidized by travel time, childcare costs, and especially loss of time from work. The difference between provincial health ministry policies and those of the workers' compensation boards illustrate this nicely.

Each province operates its own Workers Compensation Act independently, but each faces the same dilemma. By law, the Board

(WCB) is liable for *all* the costs pertaining to an injury that occurs at work. In other words, they pick up the tab not only for the doctor's fees and hospital charges, they also pay for medication, physiotherapy, and anything else pertaining to that injury, especially lost wages.

Much finger-pointing has been levelled recently at the WCB for having created a "second tier" of health care, because it is well known that patients with a WCB injury can get looked after faster than others—one of the legal ways to "jump the queue" in this country. In some provinces, access is possible to private surgical clinics with short waiting lists, and in other cases, WCB patients receive special treatment (such as blocked time for MRI)—even while in regular hospitals. In reality, there is a very logical explanation for what seems like "special" treatment for those lucky enough to have a WCB-related injury.

The answer is simple. WCB willingly pays a higher surgical fee to get faster care for their claimants, because it is *less expensive* than paying prolonged wage replacement costs. It is also better for the patients to get back to work as soon as possible, because those who have prolonged time off work are much more difficult to get back into the workforce. In BC, for example, the WCB often pays a higher fee to the surgeon, and another to a clinic, with the stipulation that definitive treatment must occur within 21 days of the initial assessment. As long as this time frame is met, WCB is quite content with the trade-off, because it still costs them less overall. It also happens to be better for patients. No wonder that governments, for all their rhetoric, have not closed the "second tier" that WCB represents. Nor is it likely anyone ever will. Wouldn't it make more sense to raise everyone to that same level, so we can all share in the savings?

Why do the provincial medical plans not understand this simple arithmetic? Perhaps it is because they are not paying for all the costs, the way WCB does. Lost wages, prolonged disability, and permanent harm from excessive waiting for definitive treatment are all costs borne by *us*—not by the provincial medical plans. Let's not expect anyone else to come to our rescue. As long as regular Canadians don't get this simple logic, no one else will ever lift a finger to change things.

Unfortunately for us, the costs we bear personally are also reflected in the tax revenues government receives. So while our governments pretend that they are not the ones picking up the bill for lost earnings, they ignore the decrease in productivity that results, along with the loss to the economy and to the taxes they will never collect. Maintaining collective health is not a "them-vs.-us" game—it is in all of our interests, financially as well as morally, to keep our working population healthy as much of the time as possible.

What Services Should be Excluded from SBF?

It is easy to think of some services that would become unstable if funded strictly on the basis of services provided. Some examples that come to mind would be tertiary centres for spinal cord injuries, burns, emergency ambulance services, and some mental health services. There are many others that need more stability in funding than a SBF system alone can provide.

But SBF does not imply an obligation to include *all* services through this method. In fact, there is no reason to force complete support of all of a hospital's funding through SBF alone—a hybrid system of core funding, combined with SBF, would offer virtually all of the incentive, competitive, and distribution advantages of full SBF, while maintaining the stability of traditional global methods. For example, a two-thirds/one-third mix of global and SBF funding would still preserve the incentives to provide services and the need to understand and control costs, without the pressure that complete SBF would entail. The key is to get the right mix and take advantage of the best aspects that both offer.

7. LET GO OF CONTROLS ON CAPITAL FUNDING

It is time the money generally reserved by governments and pre-destined for 'capital projects' was freely disbursed by formula to the regional health authorities so that they could spend it as they saw fit. This is one advantage in having regional authorities in the first place. This simple point, though anathema to those that embrace the *Dominant Model*, follows naturally from the service-based funding model, which pays for final product since capital investment is an essential prerequisite to the delivery of any product. This is true in private industries, and is no less true in public ones. The reasons given for separate ministry control systems for capital expenses are the usual ones: control of costs, and preserving political accountability for the choices made. Paradox-ically, both would improve once controls were removed, instead of getting worse.

Think of it. In their desire to limit spending and preserve accountability, most government institutions (and health is no exception) guard operating funds and capital monies fiercely separate. Hospitals (or RHAs where they exist) are prohibited from using money from their capital budget on operating expenses and vice-versa. Instead, they have to plan their capital spending in detail, submit it to government, and wait for approval—a process that literally takes years. Since approval is seen as such a long shot, no one should be surprised that the sub-missions tend to be inflated and somewhat grandiose, as hospi-tals try to compensate for the odds of being whittled down in some areas, or refused outright. Approval, when it does come, is usually delayed, so that the original plans have become either irrelevant or are in need of major modification—issues which are rarely addressed, for fear of threatening the approval that was so hard-won in the first place.

"Tell me again why it can't be done. We have this ageing heart cath room that is too far away from the rest of our hospital to run efficiently. We have to hire four extra people to handle the delays and the extra traffic back and forth, and can only manage to do five cases a day, even when it is running full tilt. You know the numbers. A new facility would cost us $600,000 but increase our output to 12 cases a day, with fewer staff. We would recoup the upfront cost in only three years and be helping twice as many people or more. That's not counting the savings on overtime we are carrying by having all those people waiting in the ER just because they need a heart cath."

"I've told you before. One is capital funds and the other is operating funds. We're not allowed to move money around from operations and invest it in hard stuff like bricks and equipment. We have to wait for our capital grant to come through."

"But isn't money just money? You know we've been waiting nine years now for approval. Last year, you said we would get it for sure—but it didn't happen. They gave the go-ahead to the project at the General instead."

"Yeah. They had that research unit they've been clamouring for since I don't know when. I guess the ministry figured it was more important or something. After all the work that Mary did on our submission. We all thought it was perfect. Even had the local politicians on side. Too bad. We were kind of hoping it would get approved as part of our redesign for the front entrance. Would have solved our parking lot problem, too. Do you think we made it too big by adding all those things into the submission?"

"Who knows? They seem just as likely to approve big projects as little ones. Sure hope the approval comes before all our heart surgeons decide to leave. They are so frustrated working in such a small facility."

"Don't worry. We can try again next year. Mary thinks if we bundle it together with the redesign of the emergency department, it would get a higher profile and may make the difference. The last time we got approval for something this big was eight years ago. By the time we got it, the cost of doing it had doubled. But it will be our turn again sometime. Let's make sure when it comes, that we get as many of our needs met as we can."

"Sure. But I still don't understand why we can't just move some of that money from one pot to another."

There are some capital expense situations in which the involvement of a provincial ministry makes sense, such as tertiary facilities or one-of-a-kind services. Also there are some individual hospitals, especially in the absence of a regionalized structure, that do not have the sophistication in management to address their needs without help. In the majority of routine cases, however, the forced separation of capital and operating costs makes no sense. Especially in the case of an RHA with sufficient size and budget, the available expertise is as good or better than what the ministry can provide, and the RHA is closer to both the need and its own staff resources to appreciate the detail. An example might help.

PACS is the term used to refer to computerized X-ray imaging systems that replace the old X-ray film and processing machines. Instead, they let hospitals place X-rays and CT scan images onto a computer network, accessible anywhere in the hospital or even on the Internet. The upfront cost of about six million dollars or so is generally recovered in about three years by savings on the film and chemicals and on the increasing maintenance costs of keeping the older machines that process X-ray film working. The move is a strategic one that saves money and improves service, but rigid segregation of capital from operating budgets and the need to apply to the ministry for approval impedes the managerial decision-making process. The rigid barrier between capital and operating funds should be eliminated to allow more flexibility with money, and the opportunity to make strategic decisions.

But the question of how a release of capital funding by formula would preserve accountability and keep spending in control is an important one and needs to be specifically addressed. The answer is that, as long as funding is actually fixed by formula, there should be no worries about cost, because total expenses would be unchanged. The most important single way to improve account-ability is to remove the notion that the funds are coming from someone else's money. By removing the sense of a gamble, and by making those funds the property and responsibility of the RHA in the first place, there remains no reason to inflate the proposal or pad the costs. On the contrary, one could expect the RHA to take extra care to get the most from its own money—often including the mobilization of other community resources that would other-wise have remained untapped or hidden.

The fact is, choices about capital expenses are not without risk, no matter who is making the decision. Given a reasonably sophis-ticated Regional Health Authority, second-guessing the capital expenditures of the staff in a provincial ministry adds nothing of value, and by impeding timing, can render the RHA helpless to control its own investment strategy. Under a service-based funding system, the financial viability of new projects can be estimated based on previous experience, and when one's own money is at stake, the incentives are strong to take care before funds are com-mitted. Promoting the perception of an RHA having guardianship over its own money is an important means of reducing cost as well as bureaucracy at the same time as it improves accountability.

Funds normally reserved for capital projects (outside of those reserved for tertiary projects) should be disbursed to regions auto-matically and without question, based on a predetermined formula. Periodic audits by the ministry will ensure sensible accounting practices, but the strategic decisions an RHA makes with its capital funds should be its own.

Some Cost Savings We Should be Seeing

The major worry most people have about introducing SBF is the concern that costs will skyrocket once the traditional controls are lifted. While a change to SBF could raise costs in the short run, they will not skyrocket, and they will be offset by significant savings in the long run. In the first place, there are natural limits— even if funds were plentiful—on how much can be spent. There are only so many doctors, so many anaesthetists and operating rooms, so many hospital beds and so many nurses. Even if the lid were removed, there is a limit to how much can be spent, as long as money is tied to services performed.

We mentioned already one cost saving that SBF would bring, in a reduction of the cost of the queue. There are some others:

(1) **Improved efficiency due to competition**: Although our health care "experts" may bristle at the thought of public hospitals competing with each other for work, competition is still by far the best cost-reducer we can hope for. This simple point has been demonstrated over and over, in many industries and in different economies. Even if some people find such competition among hospitals worrisome, it is much better than the current situation, in which hospitals constantly push people away or convince them to go elsewhere. Whether we acknowledge it or not, both cost and quality have been victims of the express ban on competition within health care, even among public providers in our health industry.

Canadians were in an uproar recently, over the purchase of Canadian Airlines by Air Canada. People worried that the monopoly it would create for Air Canada and the loss of competition would result in a deterioration of service and unrestrained airfares. If Canadians understand that costs in the airline industry benefit from competition, why not in health?

(2) **Local ownership:** Allowing regions more control over their capital resources would finally give them a sense of ownership that they are denied with the present patriarchal system. Projects 'owned' by a community often proceed faster, at less cost, and make better use of local resources. The one sure way to increase cost is to let people think that a project will be paid for with someone else's money.

(3) **Competitive feedback:** Since there is no way to measure productivity under the present system, there is no way for hospitals to uncover bad management practices by getting the financial feedback they need to improve. Instead, failure can always be blamed on the ministry or on lack of government funding. A competitive industry will motivate each hospital to monitor its own practices and learn from the successful methods of others.

(4) **Central planning dead ends:** Planning activities designed and controlled locally are much more likely to proceed to fruition than those conceived by someone else, as is the current practice in the most provincial ministries. Much time and money are spent under the present system on grandiose plans that are ultimately abandoned. This is all money down the drain that should have gone to actual health care services.

(5) **The Make-Work cycle:** Central planning breeds a network of bureaucratic processes, each with its own life force, and each creating more work for hospitals and for everybody else. An example is the amount of work needed to satisfy provincial

ministry staff on capital projects, described in the example above. This is an unnecessary expense, and a huge loss of time and often of opportunity. The ministry staff is rarely better placed to evaluate the submissions than the people who wrote them in the first place. Often the reverse.

(6) **Output discipline**: Under the current system, we pay for a process; under a market-oriented system, we would only pay if there were an actual end product. There is a discipline in knowing that no matter what the process used, a hospital has to actually provide a service if it wants to be reimbursed, and it has to keep its own costs competitive with other hospitals providing the same service. From the government's perspective, there is also an assurance that if money is being spent, at least the services are being provided. There is no such assurance under the present system.

8. INCREASE THE SUPPLY OF SKILLED STAFF

In the end, simply increasing pay scales will not correct the problem we are facing. The shortage of trained staff, be they nurses, doctors or technical people, can only be corrected by increasing the supply, which means investing in training programs. But remember, the shortage was caused by cuts in training positions, and these were stimulated by the desire to save money. Why now would we reverse that direction and create rising costs again?

The answer comes back to the economics lesson that all beginners learn. Creating shortages is, in the long run, the most costly mistake we can make. Unless we produce enough personnel to create some competition for existing jobs, we stand no hope of holding onto costs. The irony of the policies of the past 15 years is that they were motivated by the desire to save money, but ended up creating one of the most costly crises in Canadian history. The true extent of the rise in health-care costs is still unknown and is yet to be counted, but we can be sure that the message to the unions—nursing, medical, or whatever—is that they finally have the paymasters on the ground and at their mercy. After years of negotiating at a disadvantage, they are tired of being overworked and angry at how their industry has been abused by governments. They know they have the upper hand, as well as the support of the public. The true costs of the foolish policies of our past will gradually become apparent over the next five years, as we helplessly watch the pay settlements set new records. Let us remember how we got into this mess in the first place.

So, the cost of training new staff is a sound investment, and need not in itself be very expensive. But the process-laden methods we employ to fund health care are not an anomaly. They are, unfortunately, mirrored in the way we fund our training schools and universities. The problem with nursing training is an excellent example. Before one extra nurse is trained, the institutions that do this training will want upfront money to hire more teachers, build more classrooms, and buy more teaching tools. The costs are carefully added, so as to make sure that everything needed will be there, with enough cushion to ensure the security of the institution. Even after this money is placed in their bank accounts, there is no assurance that even one extra nurse will graduate, not to mention stay after graduation to work in that community.

There is an alternative, which is simply to offer a financial reward to the schools for graduating a nurse—a reward that is sufficiently high to motivate training institutions to redirect their existing resources in the desired direction. It is similar to the principle of funding desirable services instead of processes that might or might not produce the intended results.

The same principles are illustrated by the way the government has, in the past, kept the wolf population under control. Before anyone is offended, the example is only to demonstrate some economic principles and not to make a statement about animal rights or conservation. From time to time, the wolf population has increased to the point where the wolves outgrew their traditional food supplies and roamed into neighbouring countryside, causing damage to livestock. When this happened, governments wanted to cut back the wolf population to keep them in balance with other resources. Imagine what the cost would have been of mounting a series of expeditions, all with men trained and equipped with the best rifles and snowmobiles, to cull the wolf population.

This is essentially the way we tackle health care. Compare that scene to the usual practice, in which governments simply offered a bounty on wolves. The response was an immediate reduction in wolf population, as hunters responded to the incentive. Once the objective was reached, the bounty was cancelled—minimal cost with a maximal effect. Again, not intended as an argument for either killing or saving wolves, but the same economic principle could be put to use to increase the number of trained nurses and other staff at an affordable upfront cost.

9. DOCTORS INSIDE HOSPITALS COME FIRST

The problem of GPs leaving their practices and working in walk-in clinics was explored in an earlier chapter. A related problem is the number of doctors who are choosing to give up their hospital privileges and limit themselves to office practice. In effect, they are choosing to become "fair-weather doctors" since they continue to treat patients while they are well, but as soon as those patients are sick enough to need a hospital, they must see someone else, because their own doctor will not follow.

It was once a safe assumption that doctors would cherish the privilege of looking after their own patients in hospital. That assumption stopped being valid at least ten years ago. But what was only a trickle as little as ten years ago has now become an avalanche. Full-service general practitioners—those who follow their patients and manage them when they are sick in hospital—have suddenly become a vanishing breed. Doctors are resigning their hospital privileges in massive numbers, leaving hospitals with only specialists to do all the work. It is small wonder, since their colleagues down the street who choose to work in walk-in clinics make considerably more money with much less work, and without even having to take out-of-hours call.

The problem is not so much one in which existing GPs are changing as one in which new doctors are opting for the less diffi-cult lifestyle, leaving the older GPs just that—getting older, without a hope of finding anyone to take over their practices. The added work of maintaining a practice under dwindling manpower then begins to take its toll on those who have been conscientious GPs all their professional lives. Now, even these doctors—albeit reluctantly—are walking away from in-hospital responsibility.

The pullout of general practitioners from hospital involvement is more than just an inconvenience for those who cannot have their own doctor look after them in hospital. It is a death blow to the way doctors have traditionally learned and developed their skills.

Take, for example, a typical general practitioner from the not-so-distant past. There is a popular myth that doctors learn how to be doctors in medical school. This is a naïve joke. Doctors learn how to get started in medical school, how to be safe during intern-ship, and how to be good at what they do over years and years of practice. A typical new graduate joins a group of established physi-cians whose support keeps him (or her) safe for the first few years. Interaction with specialists—most of which occurs in hospitals—and the opportunity to follow patients and learn from their expe-rience are the fuel that drives the development from medical school graduate to a competent general physician. For those who work a conventional medical practice, that is. Those who choose a walk-in style practice with no hospital involvement deprive themselves of the main way physicians learn how to become better physicians. It is a sure way to guarantee a permanent new medical school graduate working in the same clinic for decades, with little chance of even knowing what he or she is missing. Unfortunately, the public has no way of knowing, either.

How has our cherished medicare responded to the challenge posed by this shift? Why, in no way at all. There is not even a public record of where doctors maintain privileges, nor whether they bother to maintain privileges anywhere at all. Each province has a legally-constituted college of physicians that licenses doctors and disciplines them when they fail to measure up to professional standards. These standards govern how doctors practice, how large their signs may be that advertise their skills, the rules they must respect when they compete with each other, and the ethical standards they must meet in their prescribing and in their dealings with patients. Colleges keep meticulous records of the training completed by each doctor and where it was done, which examinations were passed, and of any complaints lodged. All of this is done in the interest of protecting the public. Yet, the colleges do not even bother to keep track of whether a doctor maintains hospital privileges or not.

Not for a moment am I suggesting that doctors who limit themselves to office practice are no longer providing a service. Nor would I imply that doctors should somehow be forced to keep active hospital privileges if they do not want to. But the current situation creates two problems.

The first is a kind of false advertising. Since most patients naïvely assume their doctor will also see them if they need to be in hospital, the failure to inform patients when they enter the doctor's office whether this is true or not is a passive way of misleading the public. Second, and perhaps even more important, hospitals— except for large teaching hospitals with a large number of student physicians—are being forced to come up with the necessary cash to lure at least some doctors back into the hospital, unless they want to run a hospital without physicians. The money for this must come out of their precious operating funds, since the pot of money that governments allot to practicing physicians is generally kept separate from the one hospitals are allowed to use. The result leaves hospitals with the added burden of trying to compensate for any inadequacies in the doctors' fee schedule in addition to their own budget.

It is easy to again blame government for failing to address this problem, which everyone in the health care industry has seen coming for at least a decade. The truth is that provincial medical associations have had much to say over where money goes within their allotted fees, and none chose to protect the fees for in-hospital care—preferring, instead, to prop up the office fees which form the mainstay of their income.

The trouble is, if we don't use our public money to support hospitals, then what are we using it for? Unless we support the need for a medical infrastructure within hospitals, we are abandoning the public institutions that are here to look after us when we need it the most. In many communities, less than half of the population has a GP of their own, mostly because they cannot find one. They are all in walk-in-clinic-style practices, making much more money. It is one place where government intervention is needed—either by mandating a portion of doctors' fees for hospital use, or by ensuring the fee schedule reflects a difference between doctors who choose to keep up their hospital practice and those who don't. It matters little how it is done, but unless we find a way to reward the practice we want, it will go the way of the dodo—and quickly, too.

Although I favour a system allowing doctors free choice in their style of practice, but providing a differential fee for those who maintain hospital privileges, there is another unspoken scenario. Perhaps it is only a matter of time before someone in government decides to redefine the type of doctor that stays within medicare in a way that restricts public funds to those physicians who decide to uphold the public (i.e., hospital) portion of the system. After all, this was one of the original unstated assumptions about physicians on which medicare was founded, and now it is the most in need of protection. Physicians would still be free to choose the style of practice they want, but would no longer be able to have both the unlimited demand and certain payment that come with a publicly-funded system, and the right to ignore the needs of the hospitals.

While the medical associations would surely have an issue with such a unilateral move, it is unlikely that it would seriously dent the behaviour of the public. The appetite for primary care according to the convenience and choice of the consumer appears to be huge. Anyone who doubts this should look at the proliferation of walk-in clinics, not to mention the number of people who prefer to use alternative practitioners for primary care, without needing any financial support from government whatsoever.

Doctors working in hospitals form an important part of every hospital's infrastructure. If public hospitals are important, then public money must be directed to keep their interest in place. Once that interest is gone, resurrecting it will not be an option.

10. RECOUP THE COSTS

We started off this section suggesting that health-care costs should be segregated from the rest of provincial government revenue. The arm's-length relationship between government and health care could be insured by the formation of a crown corporation, responsible for its own budget, with a mandate to deliver health care in its own province. The advantage, besides making it more difficult for politicians to interfere with health-care decisions, would be a transparency of the amount of money really going to health services. The public can accept rising costs if they are transparent. What is most difficult for the public to accept is the systematic hiding of costs within the jungle of other expenses that all provincial governments must carry.

Once the health-care budget is sequestered in this way, it becomes abundantly clear that the total amount spent on health services must somehow be recouped—otherwise, the corporation and the entire health care delivery system itself will implode with unsustainable debt.

This is not unlike what is occurring now, so how will a crown corporation help matters? The difference is an ability to anticipate rising costs and replenish the coffers to meet the need, much like any insurance company does when it has to raise its premiums. No one likes the thought of rising premiums, but the alternative— bankrupting our health-care system—is much worse. The difference, furthermore, is an assurance that any increased revenue stream that comes to such a crown corporation will go to health care and nothing else. Without such transparency and such assurance, it would appear no different than any other tax.

Ah yes, but how to recoup the money? That question we will not try to answer here—not because there is no answer, but because there are many. Ideas for raising revenue range from simple surtaxes to separate insurance premiums. Some argue for making health services a taxable benefit. Some suggest setting up government-sponsored trust funds that pay for personal health expenses and allow consumers some choice, much as is done in Singapore. Others propose a formula that calculates an amount blended into taxes. There are many options, all with their own strong and weak points, but none with universal support. This is definitely one area that needs discussion, research, and experimentation. The only thing, on which there can be *NO* discussion, is that it *must* occur. The money must be recouped one way or another—otherwise, all of us, on all sides of the political spectrum, can kiss our beloved health-care system goodbye.

There is, in fact, a very good case for individual provinces trying out what they believe is the best system. It is probably true that one solution does not fit all, and some individualizing and adapting to local situations is the best way to go. The part that the federal government should play here is to refrain from interfering and encourage as much experimentation with different systems as possible. Since this is one area in which the best method remains to be proven, it is not helpful to begin with restrictions. It might not escape the reader's attention, then, that the current actions of the federal government and the current version of the Canada Health Act serve to do exactly the opposite of what is needed. They *ARE* suppressing discussion on various means of recouping the money, and they *ARE* pretending—at least indirectly—that recouping the money is not important.

Without a doubt, there will be a number of people who are offended by my suggestion that health care funding be placed at arm's length from government. Perhaps these people feel threatened by the loss of political control that would result, and some even worry that the corporations would be sold to private interests, precipitating the much-feared two-tiered system.

Everyone has their own demons to worry about, but such a policy direction would hardly invite anything of the kind. If anything, it could be argued that crown corporations are not necessarily independent enough, and are still too vulnerable to politicians that care to make them so. Perhaps their real concern is that such a transparency of funding would make it difficult to perpetuate the myth that health care is free, which would undermine the entire ideology on which medicare is based. In other words, health care could no longer be so easily abused by those (mostly federal) politicians who continue to do so, or by those with a political agenda. Those still depending on keeping this illusion alive would have a serious problem, indeed.

As for making the slide toward private health care a more tangible threat, exactly the opposite is the case. The single event most likely to create a private health-care system in Canada is the impending bankruptcy of the public system as we know it. And that is imminently at hand, thanks to our current practices.

The most important component of recouping cost, therefore, requires an amendment to the Canada Health Act, removing the threats related to payment for services and replacing them with what it should have contained in the first place—a fixed financial obligation on the part of the federal government, indexed to economic factors such as tax revenue or GNP. This recommendation is one that was also supported by the Romanow Report.

More astute readers will have noticed that nowhere in this book have I talked about private medicine. Not yet, at least. Before dealing with the demons that threaten us, it was important to understand what it is that we have ourselves created. Now that we have done so, it is time to examine the dreaded devil itself, in the form of *private medicine*.

The Menace and Myth of Private Health Care

It has become impossible to have a sane discussion in Canada about health care without someone raising the dreaded spectre of private medicine. The term is used almost interchangeably with "two-tiered medicine" or "American-style medicine," but in any case, the effect is usually to cut off the discussion altogether before anything can be concluded. Who is it that has bound our senses in this way, and why do we Canadians—normally sensible, educated and sophisticated in other ways—accept such a limitation on our intellect?

The question is a difficult one, because it involves an understanding of ourselves. I hope in this section to define this taboo, trace its origins, expose the part it plays in the Canadian psyche, and explain why it paralyses our imaginations. The information is not for the faint of heart, but those that are ready to see the demon's eyes should read on.

We should start by trying to agree on exactly what it is we mean by private medicine, since it can take many forms. If we mean any system in which individuals profit from the provision of health-care services, we must start again, because this is an impossible situation to escape. All of the workers in health care, from physicians to nurses, to lab technicians and even the floor cleaners who work in hospitals, profit from providing the service, but most of them take their profit home in the form of a salary. None of the people who worry about private medicine seem concerned about profit in the form of salary, but most doctors are paid by fee-for-service, rather than salary. Although many of those who are concerned about private medicine would also prefer salaries for physicians, the current practice of fee-for-service does not in itself seem to strike the same fear as the words "private medicine." What, then, are people so worried about? Why does it matter so much how people who provide health care are paid?

Or is the concern more about who pays for health care, rather than who is providing it? As long as individuals are not excluded from health insurance, and as long as that insurance pays all the costs, do we really care who is providing the services? The answer is yes, we do seem to care, because the Canada Health Act stipulates that the insurance must be publicly owned and administered. There is no room for private insurance, then, in Canadian health care—presumably because we don't trust that a private insurer will not begin to selectively exclude high-risk people. The option of mandating universal coverage by law is a cost of operating in Canada, but allowing private insurance companies to carry the financial risk does not seem to have been considered. So, accepting that the health insurance company must be government, does it matter whether the actual providers are privately owned or not, assuming that they must accept the government insurance plan as their only source of funds?

This becomes a tricky issue, because the Canada Health Act does not specifically address it. It forms the core of a problem (as viewed from the current federal cabinet) that started in Alberta and is spreading to other provinces. Even though law does not prohibit this mix of public insurance with private providers, and even though universal access is still guaranteed, the situation is attracting significant protests from Canadians both inside and outside of Alberta. Why is this so?

The Ghost Returns

The only explanation is that the concern is not about access, but about the concept of profit itself in the classical sense, in which a speculative investment results in a financial return. The owner of an enterprise invests money that pays a group of workers, and takes the difference in profit. The original investment is called 'capital,' and the term 'profit' is generally reserved for income generated through the work of others.

Many will recognize the essence of the classical Marxist philosophy that invokes a moral charge against the very existence of capital investment. But we don't live in a communist economy in Canada. Private investment is not only completely legal, it is recognized as a major driver of the economy.

Except in health care. For some reason, the moral-economic arguments of classical Marxism have been contained for us and delivered within the sector of our economy that provides our health care.

There is more to the picture than this. Every time we go to a pharmacy, we visit a private enterprise in which someone has made a capital investment, pays a group of workers, and takes (presumably) a profit. The same is true of most medical laboratory facilities, and even doctors' offices. Yet no one seems to be arguing to close down all pharmacies, laboratories and doctors' offices. According to Statistics Canada, Canadians spend $24 billion—or about 30 percent of the total health-care budget—on private health-related expenses, outside the funding envelope provided by government. These expenses include everything from health foods to prescription drugs, from prosthetics and wheelchairs to private nursing care. Not exactly life-saving heart surgery, you might say, but necessary services from the point of the users—otherwise, why would they choose to be spending their own money this way? So, the fact of capitalism itself, even within the context of health care, does not seem to be the issue. This makes this discussion easier, because it is not my intent to argue the merits of capitalist vs. socialist economies. That has been done in many forms by others and needs no repeating here.

The intent, rather, is to make the point that there is a connection with ideology. Without question, some of the people who are most vehemently arguing against private medicine—whatever that really is—are workers who stand directly to gain from a unionized, government monopoly. Some, but not all. Clearly, the protest also includes a large number of ordinary Canadians who have no connection with unions or with political ideology, and do not stand personally to gain. What is it that binds such a large group of disparate people into one common voice powerful enough to command the respect of all our political leaders?

The common thread seems to be our sense of equality of all human beings, and a sense of fairness that is central to our Canadian identity. It is the same passion for fairness that drives our court system, our social welfare system, and our democratic process itself. Quite simply, no Canadian relishes the thought of one of his or her fellow citizens being denied the basic human right of help during physical illness. The spectre of responsibility for a person being denied access to health care on the basis of inability to pay is the driving force that binds the defenders of public health care.

So much for the easy part. Virtually all Canadians agree on the principle of universal access to health care without regard for ability to pay. It is the way this is interpreted that causes all the disagreement. Within any large group, there are bound to be people with different fundamental motives. The protest movement against private medicine is no different.

Without question, there is a faction that is frankly allied with the remains of the world socialist movement. I won't go so far as to say this is a large segment, but without specifying the actual size, it is hard to ignore the overwhelming evidence that at least some of the people protesting against private health care are also active in either the trade union movement, or in other aspects of so-called left-wing politics. Their motivation may be humanitarian, or a way of securing their own jobs, or both. Another group is the politicians we elect as our leaders, who may have various ideas of their own, but who depend ultimately on the support of the electorate. Their motivation may be personal or the result of a perception of how best to survive the political climate. And finally, there is what is undoubtedly the largest component—a heterogeneous mix of ordinary Canadians without any particular allegiance to one political philosophy and without a personal agenda. What is their motivation for dropping their usual mundane daily concerns and joining the protest against private health care?

It is the oldest and most powerful weapon in any political arsenal—fear. It has driven masses of people to religious fervour, even to war. So, there is nothing unusual if the natural fears of one group are deliberately fanned by others with a different motivation. In this case, it is not a personal fear for individual safety, but the fear of living in a society that rejects humans in mortal danger. The threat that faces us is a loss of our very identity as caring people, and as a just society. No wonder the effect is so powerful and affects such a diverse group of people.

The nightmare image for Canadians is that of a shabbily dressed, ailing person left abandoned to die on the doorsteps of the very hospital that could have saved his life. To think that we could allow such an event to occur is a powerful threat to our image of ourselves as a tolerant, caring society. We may never know the individual who had to endure this personal torture, but the thought that we might have condoned it is intolerable. For some reason, the overwhelming evidence that the same scenario is right now being played out on our Canadian streets and in our public system does not have the same shock value. Increasingly, however, we are being forced to acknowledge the daily charade that ambulances in Canadian cities are facing as they look desperately for an emergency department that will accept their patients. Canadians are dying every day in ambulances that are redirected from one hospital to another, and in private vehicles that are turned away from already crowded hospitals. Why does the American scene create such fear in us while the equally horrific Canadian reality does not?

Whatever the reason, we cannot deny that it does just that. And yet it is not difficult to tell that it is merely a manipulation of our fears, because the image is always the same, and the evidence is never a point of discussion. Another sign of manipulation is how frequently the "slippery slope" argument is used. We are no longer arguing about the feared outcome itself, but about the possibility that we might provoke something that later could lead to the disastrous event. It is a most effective way to completely paralyse all innovation and firmly establish the status quo.

Courting the Devil

And now to the most difficult part of all. Even if it is fear we are responding to, what if that fear is justified? What if the concern about triggering a chain of events is true, and we are genuinely in danger of unleashing a monster that can no longer be contained? Fear may or may not be justified, but in either case, it makes rational thought nearly impossible. Once we are made truly fearful, we no longer make true choices of any kind—we simply respond to gut-level protective instincts. This is precisely the reaction that those who want to control our destinies want us to have.

We must not forget that there are those who stand directly to gain from the continued growth of the public workforce. Public sector workers and their union hierarchies gain directly from the process. Politicians, who take advantage of the posturing opportunities created, and who like to pose on the side of goodness and 'human rights,' stand to profit. Even doctors, often attacked as the proponents of private health care, actually stand to gain more from the current system of exclusive public health care than the alternative. In spite of the constraints placed upon doctors by medicare, they have done very well indeed over the years in the trade-off. In return for giving up some theoretical freedoms, they have had guaranteed payment of their fees, protection from competition, and the financial advantage of unencumbered demand. If the last part is hard to understand, imagine what the restaurant industry would give to have a captive clientele that knew all bills would be paid without question. It is no wonder that every group of doctors that looks at officially opting out of medicare eventually decides otherwise. Doctors have always done very well under medicare, and continue to do so, thank you very much.

But let us accept, for the moment, the contention that inspires the real fear about private medicine. In other words, let us accept that allowing private medicine to become established will indeed lead to a two-tiered system, in which the rich have access to services and the poor do not. It is precisely the demon that Canadians do not want to see, and the one that inspires such strong public reaction.

My point is that such a scenario can only happen if public health care is allowed to deteriorate at the same time. And if it does truly deteriorate beyond a reasonable point, no amount of lobbying or protesting will change things, because people will either not want to use it or will be unable to use it when they want to (as is often the case now). Private medicine is not a cancer that grows of its own right. It only grows if it is fed by an unfilled void that is already there. If public medicare were succeeding in its mission, private medicine would have no chance. Why should anyone pay voluntarily for a service they can get for free? True, there are always some people who think they are getting a superior service if they pay more, but the numbers are not sufficient for an industry to take hold unless they are augmented by a larger number of people who truly are not having their needs met.

This simple fact underscores a fundamental misunderstanding about how private/public competition works. Private medicine is not the threat to public health care in Canada. It is government mismanagement, and insistence on economic models that do not work, that are the real threats. It is the breaking of the medicare promise itself that threatens medicare, not the existence of an alternative. The extent to which private medicine actually spreads is simply an indicator that our public system is failing, as people are forced to resort to paying for services that were promised to them and they thought were guaranteed.

It is not only an indicator, it is also the *ONLY* indicator we have that can possibly act in a rapid enough time frame to give us any useful feedback. If I were a politician who did not want anyone to know how bad things were in the public system, I would fight to keep any alternatives out of sight. So it is with those who stand directly to gain from medicare—including some politicians and public sector unions. As for the rest of the people who genuinely fear that they must fight to keep private medicine out of Canada, they have been successfully manipulated into suppressing the only indicator that might be able to tell them when the very system they cherish is in trouble.

A Slippery Slope or Escape Hatch?

So, the classic arguments in support of private medicine—that people have a right to spend money on their health if they want to, and that private clinics decrease the queue for public health care—miss the point. Private medicine is largely *irrelevant* to the quality of our public system, except as a bystander that picks up the pieces and as an indicator of whether the public system is succeeding or not. It is not equality people should be fighting for, but simple access, which is guaranteed by law but neglected by practice (since excessive waiting lists are a form of refusal of access). Banning private medicine does not improve access for even one patient. The nightmare of patients dying outside hospitals that could save them is already here within the public medicare system today, as hospitals totter on the edge of financial ruin and too frequently fail to meet even the basic needs of their public. If the Canada Health Act intended truly to guarantee access rather than to maintain the illusion of access, the penalties would be for impeding that access, not for the choice among methods of payment.

How, then, should the law treat private initiatives in medicine? Should they be included within our current system as a second tier for the privileged? No, but there is no reason to ban them, either. It is just as much a violation of human rights to prevent someone from protecting themselves in dire circumstances as it is to push away those unable to pay at the doorsteps of the hospital. At any rate, banning private facilities outright simply guarantees that only those wealthy enough to go south of the border will have access to proper care, and administers a substantial loss to the Canadian economy to boot. Estimates are that we are losing $2 billion a year into the American economy, most of that from Ontario. This is not because Ontario has the longest waiting lists, but because Ontario has the most wealth. Even more important than the loss to our economy is the loss of information. We are suppressing the only indicator we have to let us know when our public system is falling below standards.

The real answer is that there is no reason to do anything with private medicine at all, except to monitor the number of people choosing this alternative and to set a benchmark at a predetermined level of usage for private medicine. That benchmark should ring some bells and force us to acknowledge that the public side of health care is in need of more help. Countries that have established two-tiered systems, with large and private components dominating the public ones, are that way because they are not responding to the information given to them by their citizens. There is absolutely no reason to be concerned if a small minority of people choose to spend their money this way, but every reason to be concerned if a large proportion does so. The reason for concern should not be whether some people are getting superior treatment, but that we are prevented from seeing the indicator that tells us that the public system needs more support than it is getting. With the benefits of size, legislation, and with the tax advantages that public systems have, they should have no trouble competing against a private operation unless they are seriously constrained by law.

At the same time, there is no reason why public institutions should not take greater advantage of the competitive pricing and market discipline with which private facilities must deal. This is already the case for laboratories, radiology facilities, physicians' offices, and retail pharmacies. The barrier against expanding this relationship to include surgical care is an artificial one, driven by those who want to keep jobs within the comfort zone of the public sector. Fair enough, if that is what they want to do, but it has nothing whatsoever to do with patient care. It also nails to the floor any attempts at innovation in the way this kind of service is provided.

In fact, the entire structure of the debate does us a disservice because it is not, and never really was, a struggle between public vs. private policies. If the lessons of the first chapters of this book are understood, we would see that the inefficiencies we live with in our health-care system are not unique to public systems, but can easily exist (and often do) in private systems as well. Imagine, for example, that we entered into an exclusive, long-term contract with a private corporation such as IBM for all of our computer services, in which we agreed to pay IBM not for the products they supplied, but for whatever *processes* they considered necessary to meet our needs, at whatever price they could justify. Furthermore, to ensure we remained compliant in our ignorance, the agreement stipulated that any open discussion about price or even the act of looking at another company's products would constitute a violation of the agreement. Most people would understand that entering such an agreement would be folly, and that even a well-intentioned quality private corporation, if left within this arrangement for two or three decades, would take on the same irrelevance and excessive costs we are experiencing with our public system.

It is not, therefore, the quality of 'private-ness' that creates value—it is the active competition, and the power of consumer choice, that keeps an industry cost-effective and relevant. So the term 'private,' as used within the Canadian debate about health-care, is really nothing more than a surrogate for operating in a competitive, cost-aware, consumer-focussed environment. There is really no good reason why a public corporation could not function just as effectively if working within an 'internal market' designed to provide a similar set of conditions.

Until such time as a mature internal market exists, a healthy private industry that parallels the public one and can contract with it to provide services would force both sides to work in the same competitive environment. It is, therefore, much more than a way to decant the waiting lists. It is quite simply the only 'reality check' available to tell public hospitals whether the quality of service they provide and the price at which they provide it meet acceptable standards, both to the public and the workers within the industry.

Which is why it is truly a tragedy that so many Canadians are ready to go to battle at the first sign of any private investment in health care. If their intent is to keep public hospitals and medicare healthy, they are undermining their own objectives. Their actions are merely shooting the proverbial messenger that is trying to bring them the information they need.

If we had a crystal ball that could show us the future of our Canadian health system, what would it show us? The last chapter will show us two distinctly different images. Each is possible, depending on what a relatively small number of people who hold authority ultimately decide to do.

PROGNOSIS

Two Very Different Futures

The previous chapter laid out ten points which will ensure the survival of public health care in Canada, but only if they are implemented before the system reaches the point of no return in its collapse. How do we know when it has reached this point? The simple answer is: the point of no return has been reached when we can no longer afford what it costs to save it. Whether we are there or not is still up for debate. Clearly, some think we are there already.

In the meantime, it is not unreasonable to ask where to begin. Many of the points discussed above cost money, or at least divert resources from existing commitments. There is a risk. It might not work, either because it is too late or because the cure is not pursued with enough energy, or perhaps there is not the collective will to see it through. Any number of things could jeopardize the changeover from the *Dominant Model* to one based on an internal market. Where do we begin?

HEADS, WE WIN

Without a doubt, the single most important step toward rescuing our hospitals and making a fundamental breakaway from the *Dominant Model* is to replace the current method of global funding for hospitals with a service-based one. This simple change will reverse the current trend and ignite the fuel that fires the internal market; it will give a signal that services have a value, and those who provide services will be recognized. It will immediately shine a spotlight on hospitals that have historically consumed an excessive share of resources without producing fewer patient services than their peers. It will allow these hospitals to either change their practices or accept the consequences of decreased funding. Conversely, it will allow hospitals which have maintained high productivity to reap a financial reward, but also spur them to share the secrets of their success with others. It will install competition, since hospitals that receive identical amounts of money for similar services will need to become more efficient if they want to generate a positive cash flow. It will attract new money in the form of investment from sources other than government, since hospitals with the ability to meet the needs of the public can be assured of financial reward. It will save money by reducing the bureaucracy needed by the ministry, allowing it to be redirected toward the development of public standards, standard information systems, and a credible audit process.

It will further save money by reducing the size of the most expensive constituency we have—those people stuck waiting for medical and surgical care. These are the people who are forced to use drugs and doctors' time, who get worse while waiting, so that when they eventually do come to treatment, they cost more to look after. It will turn professional staff, physicians, nurses and technicians, from expensive burdens into valuable assets that can set their wages and fees by market conditions instead of being dependent on their unions. And finally, it will firmly establish that patients and the receivers of hospital services are entitled to be treated with respect, instead of as another cost item shoved about from one institution to another.

These are a lot of achievements to get from one small change—especially one that does not in itself necessarily cost any money. Of course, I am simplifying the process. Transitions are never that easy but the details are not important here. The reason this one move would achieve so much is because it aims at the heart of the assumptions the *Dominant Model* makes about money. Instead of assuming someone else will always pay our way, it would force us to take more responsibility. It would force us to estimate value and to count. It would force us to measure productivity and provide feedback about success. It would, in short, force us to acknowledge that money is never in abundant supply, and it would make us keep our promises.

With only this one change, the conversion of hospital funding from the global method to a service-based model would replace the COMECON model in health care with those of a market economy. Since this would disturb more than a few people, it may not happen.

TAILS, WE LOSE

The alternative scenario could just as easily unfold. In this one, money does eventually run out. The unfortunate politician who is the bearer of that bad news would be necessarily more preoccupied with the budget than with the need to reform the system. The result would be an announced across-the-board budget cut with the teeth necessary to see it through, giving the unequivocal message that spending beyond the budget would simply not be reimbursed the way it always has been in the past. The assumption behind this scenario is that hospitals (or RHAs) will never embrace painful reforms unless they have no choice—that much of what hospitals do is still not needed, or if it is, then it is more than we as a nation can afford. If put under enough financial pressure, the thinking goes, hospitals will eventually acknowledge their sins and conform. Anyway, there is a generally accepted adage in business that a five-percent budget cut is something any organization can withstand, even if it will never admit it voluntarily.

There are some attractive aspects to this approach. It maintains the status quo of government control through the health ministry, it takes no risks with unproven funding mechanisms, it puts an acceptable numerical limit on the costs government can expect to pay, and it needs little explanation to a public that has come to applaud restrictions on government spending. Unfortunately, it also further imbeds the flaws inherent within the current system, and when the time comes, will fail to meet the budget it projects for itself—no matter how sharp the teeth being used.

But we have been there before. The proposed changes masquerade as "health care reform," but are really a continuation of the *Dominant Model* that got us to this point in the first place. How do we recognize reforms that are merely dressed-up versions of the *Dominant Model*? It is admittedly easy to be fooled, since the initiatives can take many forms, but most people with a little practice can spot the telltale characteristics.

THE DEVIL WE KNOW

The first giveaway is that the ideas look good. In fact, they look very good. They are simple, filled with the buzzwords of the day, and foster a feeling of warmth and trust. Buried somewhere in the concept is a large but often understated bureaucracy. There is an implicit assumption that, for the most part, people will do what they are told. Just about always, an impressive amount of money is quoted as a single sum that has been dedicated to the project.

More significant than what is said, is what is left unsaid. No mention is made, for example, of unit value. In market systems, unit value is where things start, and the total cost of the project is calculated by adding up the unit values. The *Dominant Model*, however, works the other way around—it starts with the total dollar amounts, without an obvious method of derivation, and leaves the unit values curiously undetermined. There is no mention of incentives, and the need for such is rarely acknowledged. The consumer—if mentioned at all—is treated more like an item on an assembly line than an independent entity capable of making choices. In other words, there is no acknowledgment of a market, because the people at the controls don't think it is important.

Before readers are reminded too quickly of the Romanow recommendations, it would be useful first to to review an experience from our recent past. The federal government's Primary Health Care Transition Fund resulted from the first ministers' conference in September 2000. It placed $800 million into a series of reforms, the stated aim of which was to assist provinces to "bring about permanent and sustainable changes," including:

- Community-based primary health clinics

- More interdisciplinary teams with enhanced roles for non-physician providers

- Better linkages to hospitals, specialists, and other community services

- Increased emphasis on health promotion, disease and injury prevention, and management of chronic diseases.

It certainly met the first criterion of sounding good. How could anyone argue against such a windfall of benefits? Notice the large amount of upfront money announced as part of the package.

It should be a tip-off that something was not right. Why was it $800 million? Why not $900 million, or why not only $500 million, if that would suffice?

What was *not* said is that the plan did not exactly emanate from an agreement as such. Health care is, of course, a provincial jurisdiction, and all the first ministers to a man wanted financial assistance to use in their own province as they saw fit. The federal government had a different agenda and would only agree to pass more money to the provinces if it fit the ideology espoused at the federal level. In the end, since no one actually had anything *against* primary health care reforms in principle, they settled for the money under any circumstances. They chose to ignore the fact that the amount of money was not a calculation based on a unit cost. Indeed, there is little sense even of what a unit of service might be under the new scheme. Perhaps that is why there are no specified outcome targets by which success or failure could ever be judged. It is hard to conclude anything other than that the $800 million was politically derived, with the details to be worked out later. This will never happen. One-and-a-half years later, in spite of the number of impressive words in the original document, the details of specific service, unit cost and unit benefit, and a method for measuring success or failure have still not been addressed.

The outrage should not be over whether primary health care needs reform or not. It should be over the mechanism of funding, which fails to match cost to what is expected. No wonder we have no idea what things cost, when the ones who write the original cheques do not even bother to make a rough estimate. Instead of using a business model based on unit cost of a tested service, they play on the power of large amounts of money and the gullibility of the public that lofty ideals are indeed within grasp simply by saying so.

THE ROAD TO ROMANOW

It is not difficult to see where the final expression of the *Dominant Model*, in the form of a report by the Romanow Commission, came from. The seductive appeal of its simplicity and humanitarian language is enhanced by the fact that the model works very well as long as money is in abundant supply. But the disjoint between money and services that is fundamental to all *Dominant Model* economics ensures that costs will go one way, while services go another.

Eventually, the money really *does* run out. Then, instead of stimulating hospitals and RHAs to change their practices, the inevitable budget cuts force them, like turtles, to pull in their appendages to protect what infrastructure they still retain. Instead of creative change and risk-taking, hospitals try to protect their core projects by axing those designed to save money in the future or decongest other resources, even if they have already received substantial investment. Because there is no penalty for cutting back on services, there will be only token protection for what the hospitals are there to do. Cutting essential staff further feeds the shortage monster, since those who remain will be forced to work even harder until they hate their jobs or quit. By cutting budgets across a spectrum of departments, they will further stimulate the sub-optimization cycle described above, passing costs around the circle of providers until the total work created by the passing on of activities exceeds anything they might have hoped to save. Queues for services will grow even longer, adding even more fuel to that particular furnace of costs.

Perhaps this is all the care we can afford, or perhaps it is a stage we must go through to achieve the financial stability necessary for the system to survive. Is it really true that any industry should be able to sustain a five-percent drop in revenue without a major catastrophe?

But this is an unusual industry following unusual rules. It has already weathered a series of similar budget cuts over several years without the usual ability of other industries to respond to market shifts by raising prices. It has suffered through increasing staff and physician shortages that have raised its operating costs and alienated its workforce without any hope of recovering those costs. And finally, it is an industry that faces relentless increases in demand as the public expects a level of care consistent with the untenable promises government made in the first place. It faces these demands with a funding mechanism unable to respond to simple inflation, never mind to demographic shifts and social adjustments that affect its mandate. At some point it is going to crack.

Perhaps those who think further budget cuts are necessary and must simply be absorbed by hospitals see those hospitals as being similar to cars cruising the highway. Just as one can always slow the car by easing up on the gas pedal, it seems that hospitals, when funding is in short supply, should be capable of being throttled back to a slower speed. But hospitals are more like airplanes than cars. They can be throttled back to a point, but there is a speed at which the transition stops being gradual and becomes sudden. The aircraft is no longer flying, but stalls and goes into free-fall.

How will we know when we have reached that point? We will know because loss of staff will reach the critical point where each staff defection influences the next. Each nurse or doctor who leaves creates a worse situation, because those who stay are forced to compensate more by working even harder. At some point, the workload for remaining staff becomes intolerable, and they either physically leave also or simply give up. At that point, the entire system becomes gridlocked, with patients unable to either get in or out of hospital. Costs continue to soar in the meantime, even as fewer patients are looked after, as those who are dropped by the system try desperately to find help. Some hospitals will resort to 'dollar store' tactics, in an attempt to boost revenue, by catering to foreigners who are exempt from the restrictions of the Canada Health Act. It is the ultimate irony that the gatekeeper mechanism—the very one designed to control costs—eventually grows into a beast large enough to destroy the system that created it.

As the public system collapses, Canadians would, as the Eastern Europeans did, ignore the law and look after themselves any way they can. It would be a boon time for those interested purely in private medicine. Private health care would, of course, consist completely of fees that match perceived value—so, in a sense, this second scenario would be reverting to a service-based model anyway, much like the first. One might say, therefore, that the service-based financial model is inevitable at some time, regardless of which approach the health ministries decide to take. Only under this later scenario, government would have lost all control of fees and would have no money left with which to influence the people capable of providing medical care.

One more point. Those planning to cheer when private medicine triumphs should think again. Health models based on private medical services depend on a mature insurance system that protects people from catastrophic costs through a series of pre-set regular payments. This is precisely the kind of consumer protection that has been prohibited by our Canada Health Act from ever being developed. If the public system ever collapsed in Canada, it would occur too rapidly for this private insurance mechanism to develop. People would, therefore, fall between the cracks of a failed public system and a new private system which would not have had the time to develop an affordable insurance safety net. Few of us—even those who are reasonably well off—could withstand the full financial blow of a major illness without insurance of some sort. All of it adds up to a grim picture.

Conclusion

We started this book with the fall of the Berlin Wall. As we complete our travels through the history of medicare, how well does the comparison hold?

We know that the East Berlin authorities built "the Wall" in 1965 because too many East German citizens were leaving the communist dream for freedom offered by the West. They were fleeing a country which dedicated two of its generations to achieving the humanitarian principles of equality by putting their faith in a new and unique set of economic rules, embodied within the activities of COMECON. The rules essentially banned money (foreign money at least), eradicated the profit motive from commercial enterprise, and made the supply and distribution of goods an activity forbidden to all except government. In effect, this made government the only employer within the world of COMECON, since all other investment and commercial transactions were banned. Elitism in the common sense, of privilege for those with money, was eliminated in a stroke of the constitution (although it resurfaced later, in the form of privileges for those with political positions).

The regime had some impressive initial successes. The recognized credits included the organization of eastern Europe's railroad and electric-power grids; the creation of the International Bank for Economic Cooperation to finance investment projects jointly undertaken by two or more members; and the construction of the "Friendship" oil pipeline, which made oil from the Soviet Union's Volga region available to the countries of eastern Europe. Needless to say, it participated in the creation of one of the world's recognized 'superpowers,' with a political and military influence spanning the globe. By the late 1980s, the East German regime was ranked 17th in the world in GDP per person. It seemed—at least to any superficial scrutiny—that the East German equivalent of the Fathers of Confederation had succeeded completely in their dream of creating a society based on human equality. Why, then, were so many common people fleeing to the West in numbers large enough to make the East German authorities build a physical wall to keep them in? Why were not at least as many people fleeing in the opposite direction?

It is now the year 2003. Back in Canada, we are dealing with a system founded in the 1960s with similar humanitarian intent, but with its scope thankfully limited to medical care rather than the entire economy. The escapees are people, unable to find an acceptable level of care, who seek medical care in the U.S. or elsewhere. The economic escapees also include a small army of physicians, nurses, and other skilled workers, who are choosing to emigrate to more lucrative jobs in the U.S. It is estimated that almost 20 physicians emigrate to the U.S. for each physician that comes to Canada, and the ratio for nurses is 15 to 1 (Sources: U.S. Immigration and Naturalization Service and Citizenship Canada). Other people who might be considered 'refugees' are the thousands who use various means, including personal connections, to quietly bypass the waiting lists imposed by official health services.

"The Wall," in Canada, is not a physical one, but a legal one that consists of the Canada Health Act and various other laws (such as the Medicare Protection Act in BC) that prohibit anyone from creating avenues for health care outside those sanctioned and funded by government. It is reinforced by Canadian tax laws, which funnel funds we thought were going into health care into federal revenues that are only partially returned and even then under conditions created for political purposes. And now the latest attempt to reinforce the Wall has arrived in the form of the Romanow Report, itself, which combines the power of the Prime Minister's Office with the temptation of more of our own money.

In a sense it should be no surprise to us that our Canadian system, founded on the same humanitarian ideals that created the socialist societies of Eastern Europe, was married to the same set of economic principles common within socialist politics of the 1960s. They form the basis for the *Dominant Model*, which has hijacked our intellect when it comes to even discussing anything to do with health care. To this day, Canadians also ban any financial transactions or even talk of money within the context of health care. Through our governments we create central planning monopolies, in the image of COMECON, empowered to direct all aspects of our health care. We ban any semblance of private initiative from it, and we cry out if any entity other than government itself dares to be an employer.

Noble principles, but they are also the ones that have failed in every jurisdiction in which they were enforced, and the same ones that are now discredited in every other country—even those with impeccable socialist credentials. Only two other countries besides Canada still ban medicine outside the paradigm controlled by government. These are Cuba and North Korea—hardly models of success for the 21st century. Why should we think Canada should be an exception to rules that govern economics in the rest of the world? The sad truth is that Canada is no exception, and the history of our health-care system will eventually follow the path of the Eastern European economies. But we lag by a decade or so.

I do not fault the original founders of medicare, nor do I quarrel with their intent. But we could have learned from consequences others have endured. We could, at some point, have modified the economic rules for our medicare system. Like other (notably European) countries, we could have learned from the financial collapse of the socialist model and modernized the financial basis of our medicare system to make sure the original objectives remained secure. We could have jettisoned the politics and created a funding formula that was honest and made only promises that could be kept.

Instead, we have allowed ourselves to become imprisoned within the *Dominant Model* by those who stood to gain from the pretense of humanitarian intent, in spite of all the evidence that it was unworkable. It has been a long process, spanning three decades, multiple administrations, and different parties from various points in the political spectrum. We cannot accuse just one or the other—all share in the blame. But above all, we have to blame a gullible public for accepting the paralysis that went with the fear of becoming like Americans, and accepting the pressure tactics of those who stood to gain from the status quo.

Can medicare still be saved? I believe it can, but only if we are prepared to accept some collective loss of face and only if we are prepared to risk some new initiatives. The reintroduction of market principles through an internal market will never be a feature of the current thinking which dominates the health care industry. It will require a unique kind of political leadership, and it will unfortunately cost money. Most of this cost is not avoidable, since it is the consequence of neglecting investments we should have been making for a long time.

A fix to public medicare is not inevitable, and certainly not something we can take for granted. Canadians are under a lot of pressure to enact so called 'health-care reforms' which are not true reforms at all, but a continuation of the *Dominant Model* ideology that brought us here in the first place. The people who push these ideas want to reinforce the wall and build it even higher. In order to recognize these pressures for what they really are, Canadians must have some sense of history. They must also understand that true reform never comes from stakeholders. It comes from consumers or, when consumers have been suppressed for a long time, it comes in the form of a popular revolt. Once in a while, if we are extremely lucky, it comes from a leader with unusual vision.

Not all stories have a happy ending. This one is still ours to make.

About the Author

Les Vertesi is a career emergency physician with over 25 years of experience in major trauma referral hospitals, and with a proven track record for leadership and innovation.

Perhaps best known for founding the Advanced Life Support paramedic ambulance program of the BC Ambulance service (1975 to 1985), he was also the founding chairman of the Canadian Medical Association's accreditation committee that set national standards for ambulance training in Canada. In 1978, he published the first Canadian research article to prove that paramedic skills really save lives. He became the first recipient of the Justice Institute of BC's Joseph Cohen Award for Outstanding Contributions to Public Safety (1999) for this work.

In addition to his medical degree from the University of Toronto (1970), he received a specialty certificate in Emergency Medicine from the Royal College of Physicians and Surgeons of Canada in 1985. In 1989 he added to his university training with a Master's Degree in Health Sciences and Clinical Epidemiology from the University of British Columbia, specializing in computer modeling and simulation.

His interest in international economic models expanded during the years 1985 to 2000, with a series of studies undertaken through the Danish International Studies (DIS) Institute in Copenhagen, which included visits and interviews in many of the major Eastern European capitals during the final years of the Soviet era, and then the years of recovery that followed. It was the relevance of these economic models to Canadian healthcare that became a haunting thought and eventually led to this book.

In addition to private consulting for hospitals and for the World Bank, Dr. Vertesi served as head of the Department of Emergency Medicine at the Royal Columbian Hospital in New Westminster, BC, from 1989 to 2001. He is currently the Medical Administrator of that hospital. He has maintained his clinical work during all of these years and continues to work in the Emergency Department.